C000194025

LIFE EN
& THE EMOTIONS

How to Release Your Hidden Power

John Diamond, M.D.

Eden Grove Editions

Contents

Contents

Acknowledgements

I wish to express my thanks to my students and patients, from whom I have learned so much over the years, and hope that to some extent I have repaid that debt. Much of the information in this book has been their gift to me, for which I am most grateful.

I would like to thank Virginia Rohan Mann for her help with the early draft; Dr. Gloria Schwartz for her assistance in the earliest stages of research on the relationship between the meridians and the emotions; Victoria S. Galban, my research assistant; and Harvey Klinger for his continuing advice and support.

My thanks as well to J. Frederick Smith for his kindness and his excellent photographic work. My continuing gratitude goes to Dr. George Goodheart, the originator of kinesiological muscle testing.

John Diamond, M.D.
Valley Cottage

Foreword

It is now nearly twenty years since I started working on this book. And on re-reading, it still by and large fulfills the expectations I had for it back then.

Firstly, it is a re-statement of the ancient philosophy of healing, as distinct from the usual medical goal of the mere relief of symptoms.

This Life Energy is the Healing Power Within that we all possess. And the task of the healer is not to impose his potions on the sufferer but instead to help him to actuate his own Life Energy—to help him to heal himself.

The Life Energy flows through the body mainly via the acupuncture system, and the second purpose in writing this book was to show the relationship between the meridians and the emotions.

Most illnesses start with a particular negative emotion which is then mediated via the acupuncture system to the particular organs, muscles and tissues sub-served by the particular meridian associated with that particular negative emotion. Thus by recognizing and overcoming the specific emotion, the Life Energy in the associated meridian is released and actuated. And then healing can occur.

This book; is, I believe, the first to link specific emotions, positive and negative, to particular acupuncture meridians, and thus to their associated organs, muscles and tissues. This work has now stood the test of a quarter century of clinical experience. It adds a new dimension to acupuncture, but even more so to psychiatric and clinical psychology and psychosomatic medicine—in fact to all branches of treatment and healing.

Thirdly, I have tried to accurately delineate and define the major emotions, which few others, to my knowledge, have attempted. And, furthermore, to especially relate each to its distant etymological origin and its persistence as such in our present-day unconscious. As far as I am aware, this is the only book to do so.

A word of caution concerning the testing. The test itself is inherently quite simple. However, there are a large number of variables in the tester, the subject, and the testing environment, that must all be controlled for the test to have solid validity.

In this preliminary outline, I meant the test to be used only in a domestic setting. Without intense and thorough training, it should never be employed in any professional or pseudo-professional situation. Furthermore, it is not at all necessary to get involved in the testing to comprehend the major points of the book, such as I haste outlined above.

May you enjoy reading it as much as I enjoyed writing it, for I love working with the emotions, and, as you will see, I love words. And may your Life Energy be enhanced by the reading—for that was my primary intention.

Before You Read This Book...

Get yourself a partner, friend or family member, and try the following simple test.

1. Have your partner stand erect, right arm relaxed at his side, left arm held straight out, parallel to the floor.

2. Face your partner and place your left hand on his right shoulder to steady him. With your right hand, grip his extended arm just above the wrist.

3. Tell your partner that you are going to push on his arm, as he tries to resist with all his strength.

4. Push down on his arm quickly and firmly, just hard enough to feel the spring and bounce in the arm. In nearly every case, the muscle will test strong.

Now perform the test again as your partner does one of the following things:

- Thinks of something unpleasant
- Thinks of his job
- Thinks of needing money to repair his car
- Looks at a fluorescent light
- Eats some refined sugar

The result will be dramatic. In nearly every case your partner will be unable to resist the pressure. His arm will go down easily. Although you are using the same amount of pressure, the arm goes weak.

What has happened? Somehow the thoughts and the external stimuli have reduced the life energy and caused the muscle to test weak. The same phenomenon would occur with any other muscle in the body. (This particular muscle, the deltoid, is used because it is convenient to test.) As you will learn in this book, by testing this muscle, a procedure that takes no more than a minute, it is possible to assess accurately and then to correct instantly the negative emotional attitudes affecting us at a given time. The test is basically a test of life energy.

In this book you will be shown points on the body that you can test by using the indicator muscle (the deltoid is used throughout) and one of these points. Each of these body test points, which are acupuncture meridian points, relates to a specific emotional state. Thus you will be able to determine with just a minute of testing which organs of your body are under stress; but more importantly, *you will know the specific emotional attitudes affecting you at that moment.* You can refer to the chart given you, say the corresponding positive affirmations, and reinforce them in the ways outlined—*and instantly overcome your negative mental attitudes.*

As an example, test your partner's thymus gland. Use the deltoid muscle of your subject's left arm as the indicator, and have him place his right hand on his thymus test point. If his thymus tests strong, have him think of someone he hates, or a situation of great fear. On re-testing you will find that now he tests weak. You can test other points on the body, with your partner thinking the same thoughts, and the indicator muscle will not be weak, showing us just how accurately and precisely the body points relate to specific emotional states.

Now test your partner again while he is looking at the fluorescent light. He will most likely test weak. Perform the same test again, but ask him also to think of someone he loves while you are testing him. Now you will most likely find that he tests strong!

In this book you will learn how to correct negative emotional states. For example, if your thymus tests weak, stop and think of someone you love. You will probably find that it will then test strong. There are positive thoughts and affirmations for each body point, each emotional state.

Carried out regularly, the program outlined here will not only help to keep you in correct mental balance, both in terms of correcting your emotional states and balancing your cerebral hemispheres, thereby increasing your creativity, but it will also keep your physical body healthier because all the meridians relate to your physical state as well. Therefore, with these simple techniques, which take but minutes each day, you can be well on your way to achieving positive health and optimum life energy.

Introduction

I write this book from twenty-five years of psychiatric and preventive medicine experience. Having at last reached the top of some small hill on my professional journey, I can now for the first time clearly see the goal that lies ahead of me for the attainment of perfect health for my students, and I look back into the valley from which I have thankfully arisen. Many of my years in medicine were times of disappointment, regret, and unhappiness. You will later learn precisely the meaning of these emotional states as they affect each of us and how they affected my mental and physical well-being.

I was experiencing these negative emotions because I recognised that what I was doing, and what my colleagues were doing, was not really getting anyone well. Thus it is that when I test my professional colleagues—and now I have tested many thousands of them—I find that they, too, hold negative emotions about their profession. When they think of their work experience, the job to which they are dedicated—helping mankind to reduce suffering and increase happiness—negative emotional attitudes are produced. They are not necessarily identical to those that I felt, but they are similar. Doctors go into medicine with a deep concern and love for mankind and a wish to help them overcome their suffering in the same way that a Yehudi Menuhin takes up the violin out of a great love for music and a wish to express this to the world. Yet we find today that when we test doctors, as you will be able to test yourself after reading this book, their work takes away their life energy and de-vitalises them. Imagine if the same were true for Yehudi Menuhin. Imagine that every time he thought of playing the violin, of carrying out his task in life, he lost life energy!

This was the state I was in. My life energy was draining away, and I was descending lower and lower into the valley, becoming more disillusioned, knowing that I was not achieving what I had set out to do in medicine. I was "successful" with my patients, but the positive results I achieved were basically short-lived. Too much depended on me, on the visit to my office, and so little depended on the people I was treating. Something was missing in the doctor-patient relationship.

A turning point for me occurred one day when I was in the doctors' lounge of the hospital talking to a fellow psychiatrist. He announced that the only reason a certain patient of his was still alive was because of what he said to her. In essence, he believed that he was keeping her alive! Suddenly my disappointment, my regret, and my unhappiness reached a peak (or depth, as you wish), because I realised that this was what we were *all* doing. We had this idea that what *we* did kept the patient alive, or cured him. Yet we all found that most of our patients who were sick enough to be hospitalised would later need to be re-hospitalised. The pattern seemed to be set. The hospitalisation had helped to allay or overcome the effects of the stress of their lifestyles on them, but it was the rare case where we could raise the life energy enough to make the patient so invulnerable to stress that when he returned to his domestic and work situations he was able to remain centred and strong. The disappointment over this was one of the factors leading me into my present investigations and the writing of this book.

I had walls and walls of psychiatric and medical books and journals reminding me of how much I had learned. But in order to implement this knowledge with the patient, I first had to activate his own will to be well. I had to activate his life energy. As I later discovered, this is a property of the thymus gland. We shall discuss this relationship later.

As I continued in my practice, I watched the lines on my face develop. The line of unhappiness appeared, and the lines of self-doubt, of professional guilt, of wondering constantly what I was doing wrong. I kept asking myself why my patients were not fully matured, adult, evolved, healthy and strong, invulnerable to stress, and able to face the world with a physical and psychological shield protecting them from major environmental assault. This is what I knew was their lot, and this is what I yearned for, and worked for, and was so anxious for them to have. But it did not occur. Hence the unhappiness and the sense of professional unworthiness and guilt.

This was my valley of disillusionment, of discontent, of unhappiness, and even depression concerning my work. But nearly all the thousands of my colleagues whom I have tested are to some degree experiencing a similar valley. Soon you will understand the precise meaning of these emotional states, and you will learn how to overcome them, whatever the particular causes may be.

Some years ago my life changed, and for this I am eternally grateful. When you learn what the feeling of gratitude does to raise life energy, you will recognise the importance of that statement. For the first time, I discovered that it was possible for me accurately and instantly to find the precise emotional attitudes affecting myself or my patients, and in fact, to pinpoint them for anyone, including my professional colleagues. With a few moments of very simple testing, anyone could learn for himself or herself the emotional attitudes that were holding him or her back. Thus it was that I discovered the negative emotional attitudes in my life that were holding me back personally and professionally. This is quite remarkable. It was the first time that I or anyone could learn his or her own conscious and unconscious attitudes—accurately and instantly. And the technique is so simple.

After all my years of psychotherapeutic and psychoanalytic experience, once I was able to identify my own negative emotional states, through testing I could then discover precisely which aspects of my personal and professional life were causing them. Just as importantly, I learned how I could very quickly, almost instantaneously, overcome those hindrances. The change in my outlook on my profession was immediate and striking. At this point I began to emerge from the valley. I was beginning to find the answer to assessing and enhancing life energy.

I then started to implement this testing with patients. To my great joy—and you will learn exactly what that state implies—I found that my patients, even those cases that I had been treating for years, began making dramatic improvements and recoveries. This was primarily due to the fact that I was able to help them discover the basis of their problems.

The basis of all physical and, of course, mental problems is the emotional attitude. As long as we can keep our emotional attitudes positive, as long as there are no negative patterns holding us back and draining our life energy, then we will be, and will stay, healthy and vital. We are now able to do this. Patients can be shown exactly what their negative emotional attitudes are. I have learned and shown them that with the *power of the word* (and this you will realise when you test for yourself, they are able instantly to transmute their negative emotional states into positive ones, to completely turn around the flow of their life energy from negative to positive.

It is not a question of "working through" some psychiatric problem such as why they hate their mothers, or why they couldn't get along with their fathers, why they are impotent, or whatever. It became a question of discovering the precise negative emotional state and, through the power of the word and its underlying thought, through the positive affirmation, then instantly transforming the negative framework into the positive. After seeing by testing that it worked, that it had made the difference to them, they then carried out a simple daily program to keep themselves well. And the results I found in psychiatric cases as well as with many types of disease were quite remarkable.

The big breakthrough had occurred. It was no longer a question of my doing the work for the patients. Instead I now showed the patients what their negative emotional attitudes were, and through testing I showed them where the stress problems were in their lives. More accurately, *their bodies showed us.* They saw instantly what their true wishes and desires were, and they saw how they could overcome any negative obstacles. Then they had to use their own willpowers to maintain a positive balance and thus to have a complete life change. It was a matter of their assuming responsibility for themselves, of saying, in essence, "Here I am at this point in my life; I now realise things are wrong with me and that is why I have come to the doctor. My body, through his assistance and testing, has shown me the attitudes and stresses that are holding me back. Now I make the decision that I really want to be well because I have seen how it can be done." The patient would then in a sense roll up his sleeves and say, "Let's get down to work. I see what's wrong. I see what *I* have to do to correct it, and I would like your assistance in doing it."

No more was it a matter of my feeling that it was what I did that kept a patient alive. Furthermore, if the patient did not improve, I no longer felt it was my fault. The factors that were causing my professional disappointment, unhappiness, and guilt were now abolished. Instead, there was contentment with my work, happiness, and a sense of worth, fulfilment, and purpose. My major role was to help the patient's body show him what he was doing to contribute to his illness and then to help activate his willpower, his desire to get himself better.

One of the biggest problems facing present-day psychiatry is the fact that throughout all the interviews the patient is encouraged to dwell on the negative, to tell the psychiatrist about all the bad that has befallen him, enumerating this in great detail. Such psychotherapy and psychoanalysis may continue over a period of years. The end result of this for most patients is that they become more aware of what is wrong with them, but their life energy stays low—as does that of the psychiatrist. The insalubrious effects of this have previously been discussed in my book, *Your Body Doesn't Lie.* What is required is not the dwelling on the negative. We must, of course, recognise and understand the negative. But then we give it up, transmute it into the positive. In this, way it is possible to heal oneself, quickly and very effectively. It will not be accomplished by continually dwelling on the negative. One of the primary forces leading me out of my own valley was the change from dwelling on the negative to embracing the positive. When this happened, the patient's life energy increased and so did mine. We each began our ascent.

The testing that I have mentioned has now been taught to many thousands of patients and students with wonderful, rewarding results, some of which you will read about in this book. We have also taught many practitioners of all branches of the healing arts with similar results. What you will learn can change your life, whether you be a layman or a professional, whether you be sick or well. For the first time you will learn of the stresses, conscious and unconscious, that are creating in you certain emotional attitudes that are holding you back. "Unconscious" means that you are not aware of these factors, but now you can find out for yourself the unconscious, unknown attitudes—the answer that is within yourself. This knowledge can take some years of psychoanalysis to discover. Now you can do it instantly. *For the first time, you can find your unconscious motivations, your true desires in any situation.*

From the little hill on which I find myself after emerging from the valley, I now see a goal in the distance, which I hope this book will help to accomplish—and that is the emancipation of mankind from doctors, in the sense of the doctor-patient relationship as we know it today. Except in traumatic and acutely ill cases, I hope to see the end of "patients" and the beginning of "students." In this way the doctor can accomplish his calling as teacher (the Latin *doceo* means I teach), and the patient can be transformed from the sufferer (the Latin *patior* means to suffer) to the student (the Latin *studere* means to study, be diligent), wanting to learn more about himself, wanting to help himself become mentally, physically, and spiritually as well as he can possibly be. This goal is becoming more and more attainable, possible, and realistic. I have written this book in an attempt to help you become a student—to share with you the results of my years of experience in medicine, psychiatry, and this newer work.

As you read this book you will learn many things about yourself and about the wondrous functioning of your own mind and body. You can learn how to be master of yourself, to find out exactly your level of emotional functioning, and what you can do to improve yourself. There is no need for you to stay in your valley. You will learn what you, and others, really think and really desire. You will be able to discover your true wishes, not just those in that small part of you of which you are consciously aware, but also those in that infinitely larger part, your unconscious. Once you know this, you will be in a position for the first time to make creative decisions about your life, all decisions—major and minor. You will be able to move in harmony with your true wishes and desires. You will be able to find your real self, to achieve your own individual goals on this earth. And you can determine these goals simply, easily, and accurately.

By learning your negative emotional states, you can transform or transmute them into positive ones. You will be able to release the energy that is now blocked inside you, trapped by your own thoughts, and become free and vigorous. This freedom will allow the emergence of your true self. Through understanding the incredible functioning of your own mind and body, you will learn of the power of thoughts to heal or to weaken. Through getting in touch with your own mind and body, you will find new freedom. You will discover what it feels like to have your whole brain working, to be on the path of creativity and health.

Most of our daily stresses, the factors that gradually wear down our energies, affect us unconsciously. Since they are not really known to us, we find it difficult to confront and surmount them. Now, through simple testing techniques, you can identify your own unconscious stress areas and overcome them. For example, thinking itself is often a stress factor! When we have a problem, we think on it to try to solve it, yet that very act of thinking may for many people introduce a new stress—and thinking about the problem actually becomes a problem! This can be overcome—you will learn how to make your thinking creative. You can solve problems rather than perpetuate them. Furthermore, your aspiration to be creative, healthy, and fulfilled will be rekindled and you will *want* to make the choices that will be most beneficial.

You will learn how to be creative in all aspects of your life. You will be able to apply *all* your mental energies to your daily tasks rather than using predominantly one cerebral hemisphere as 95 percent of us do 95 percent of the time. Daily activities as well as life patterns become harmonious, flowing, and energising—not just for ourselves but for others as well.

Most important of all, you will learn the power of love, how love will activate your life energy as no other force can and how it will overcome any imbalances and disharmonies in your mind or body, how love can restore you and keep you in perfect health. This is the supreme answer that is within us.

All this and more is what I mean by *psychobiological harmony. Harmony* is when "all parts are joined together for the good of the whole." I use the word *psycho* first since it refers to mental activity and, in the older sense of *psyche*, means soul. By *biological* I refer to all the physical properties and functions of life. By *psychobiological harmony* I refer not only to our totality of body, mind, and soul—the harmony between these three interdependent parts (if we can separate them at all)—but also to the harmonious working of all the parts within each. When all the parts of our psychological functioning are co-ordinated and whole within themselves, then the energy flow through our bodies will be balanced and co-ordinated.[1] In this state, there can be perfect health, happiness, and love.

I have learned from my years in psychiatry that illness is basically a problem of loving and of being loved. This was perhaps first stated by the Greek philosopher Empedocles about twenty-five hundred years ago.[2] What Empedocles said is so basic and yet at best we pay it lip service. He said that there were two forces that controlled the entire function of the universe, be it the universe of an individual—his body, mind, and soul, what we might call the micro universe—or the macro-universe of the total universe. These two forces were love and hate, if you will, the positive emotions and the negative emotions.[3] When hate is operant there is chaos and disharmony. The parts that make up the total world, the sphere, are not working together for the common good. There is fragmentation, scattering, and chaos, disharmony and ill health. But when love is operant there is integration, health, and harmony. This is my philosophy and what I hope to teach with this book—how to determine the specific areas of stress, chaos, negativity that are holding you back and preventing you from being totally healthy by preventing you from totally loving, and then how to transmute these into perfect harmonious balance.

While in this brief introduction we have covered many areas generally, the details to come will clarify any questions you are beginning to form. The goals described above are immediately attainable. The ultimate beauty of this work is that you need not take my word for any of it. Everything you learn from reading this book will be a result of the testing that *you* do. Do not take my word for it—test and prove it for yourself. After all, this is the ultimate scientific proof, whether you, in your own home—your laboratory—with yourself and your friends as your research subjects, can reach the same conclusions and achieve the same results that I and my professional colleagues have been achieving with our patients and ourselves for quite some years. The final arbiter is your own body.

One of the findings that is especially exciting in this work is that we can now demonstrate specific relationships between the mind and the body—that specific emotional states affect specific body organs.[4] All doctors, particularly those concerned with psychosomatic medicine, have been interested in this concept for many years. Now it is possible to see how this occurs.

The connecting link is the acupuncture system. I am well aware that modern Western medicine has not yet "scientifically validated" the acupuncture theories to its own satisfaction, but remember that they have been practiced successfully in China and other Eastern countries for many thousands of years. Once you have seen a major surgical operation performed solely under acupuncture anaesthesia, questions of the Western acceptance of acupuncture become insignificant. It is there and you see it. Through our research we have been able to demonstrate that each acupuncture channel, or meridian, relates to a specific emotional state, and by the very simple testing of these channels we can learn what our own emotional states are. This is a major breakthrough.[5] Once you have learned the simple testing techniques and balancing methods, you will have another tool to use in practicing positive health.

I shall delineate precisely and exactly each emotional attitude for each channel of acupuncture energy. You will learn the explicit meaning of the words describing these emotions, because I have found that the more clearly we understand these words, the better equipped we are to differentiate between them in our own minds. If we understand the difference between, for example, the states of unhappiness and depression, then when we find on testing that one of these states applies to us, we will be in a better position to correct the imbalance. Contained in the heritage of our language are the emotional truths of our civilisation. When we know the words, we know ourselves and can help ourselves as never before.

It is my hope that as you read this book you will for the first time gain an awareness of your precise emotional balance—something almost as individual as a fingerprint. Through discovering your true self and applying your knowledge about your own mind and body, you can begin to heal yourself. So it is that I would like to see my own profession—that of doctor and particularly of psychiatrist—disappear. My colleagues and I want to be *teachers* for you. We want to teach you the wonders of your own mind and your own body, and how they interact, and to show you how to discover for yourself those factors that are holding you back, preventing the optimal expression of your true self. After you have demonstrated these findings to yourself, you will have the strength of will to release the negative emotions and embrace the positive. Then you will be truly creative and on the path to positive health and maximum energy.

While this book may appear "easy," it has important psychiatric implications. Much of the work here corroborates some of the deepest, most profound, and fundamental theories of psychoanalysis and psychotherapy. So at the same time it is both apparently superficial and yet theoretical and academic. I believe scholars in psychology, psychoanalysis, communications theory and all members of the healing profession can derive much from these findings. But the book is written for *you* to help you to maximise your potential, release your energies, and become truly creative, balanced, and of greatest service to your fellow man.

All aspects of *you* will be harmoniously integrated, balanced between body and mind (both the conscious and the unconscious facets), and spirit—psychobiological harmony. It was expressed so well by Empedocles long ago:

> in the strong recess of Harmony,
> established firm abides the rounded Sphere,
> exultant in surrounding Solitude.

I hope that you will learn how to achieve this as you correct your negativities and activate your life energy.

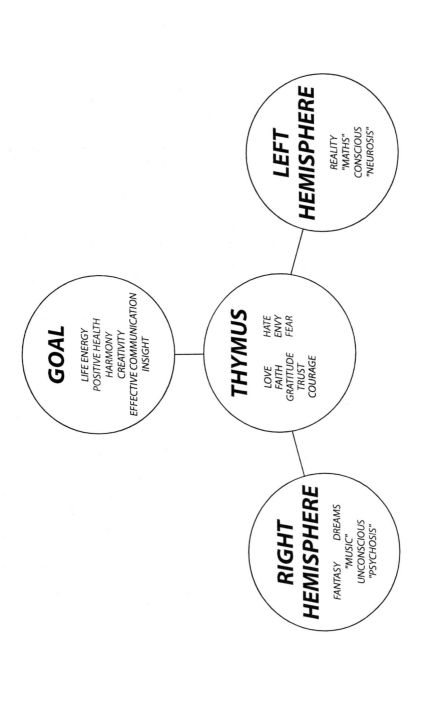

BILATERAL MERIDIANS

Meridian	Positive	Negative
LUNG	Tolerance	Intolerance
LIVER	Happiness	Unhappiness
GALL BLADDER	Love	Rage
SPLEEN	Faith in Future	Anxiety about Future
KIDNEY	Sexual Security	Sexual Indecision
LARGE INTESTINE	Self-Worth	Guilt

MIDLINE MERIDIANS

Meridian	Positive	Negative
CIRCULATION-SEX	Renunciation of Past, Generosity, Relaxation	Jealousy, Sexual Tension, Regret, Remorse
HEART	Love, Forgiveness	Anger
STOMACH	Contentment	Disappointment, Disgust, Greed
THYROID	Lightness	Heaviness, Depression
SMALL INTESTINE	Joy	Sorrow, Sadness
BLADDER	Peace, Harmony	Restlessness, Impatience

Part 1

The Goal

The Goal

It is every person's birthright to develop their true potential and aspire to evolve fully. This is our goal along the path of life and it is toward the goal that we may move if we cultivate only positive emotional attitudes and positive physical, mental and spiritual health.

Reaching toward the goal can be achieved by reducing stress, raising life energy, balancing the cerebral hemispheres, gaining true creativity, activating the thymus gland, and balancing the acupuncture meridians. In sum, eliminating the negative and promoting the positive will help bring about the attainment of the goal.

Among the most important measures we can take in order to achieve the goal is to reduce stress. This is vital. Depending on the nature of the stimulus, there are basically three effects of stress on the body: reduction of thymus activity and overall life energy, cerebral imbalance, and meridian imbalance caused by a specific negative emotional attitude created by the stress. And over the years, stress allows negative emotional patterns to be established and set. This is the root of all disease, the diminution of life energy.

But it is to health that we aspire and so our goal is to raise the life energy, not permit it to dwindle. And so our research includes the study and delineation of emotional attitudes, stress, and other factors that lead to a diminution of life energy. From this, we can develop methods for overcoming these factors and raise the life energy.

How Do We Define Life Energy?

It is life energy that causes us to grow. It is life energy that enables us to heal. Hippocrates called it the *vis medicatrix naturae*—the healing power of nature. Paracelsus spoke of it as the Archaeus. It is Prana, Chi, Spirit. It evokes the true and only healing, that which occurs from within. A drug may relieve the symptoms of a disease but it does not cure. The true cure always involves a major change in the person's attitude toward himself and toward life.

Life energy enters our body through the breath. It is life energy that flows through the acupuncture meridians and vitalises the organs and tissues. An imbalance of the flow of this life energy leads ultimately to disease. As you will learn, these imbalances come about as a result of physical and psychological factors. Through your mental powers you have the ability to rebalance the flow of life energy throughout your body and thus combat disease and keep yourself well. Life energy is breath.[1] Life energy is spirit.[2]

According to the *Oxford English Dictionary*, spirit is the animating or vital principle in man and animals; that which gives life to the physical organs; the breath of life. Thus Milton in *Paradise Lost* wrote, "The pure breath of Life, the Spirit of Man." This life-giving essence, this activating factor underlying our maturation and our vitality, our very being, is mentioned in Genesis: "Then the Lord God formed a man from the dust of the ground and breathed into his nostrils the breath of life. Thus the man became a living creature." That which causes us to live is life energy, the spirit.

Throughout the Bible we find references to the relationship between breath and spirit. The Hebrew term *ruah* comes from a Semitic root, *ruh*, signifying "to breathe," "to blow." The primary signification of *ruah* is "air in motion," as wind or breath, and the general idea which is common to nearly all its usages is "power in manifestation, or energy."[3] In Ezekiel 37:5 we read, "I will put breath into you, and you shall live," and in I Corinthians 6:10, "Do you not know that your body is a shrine of the indwelling Holy Spirit, and the Spirit is God's gift to you?"

When we are healthy we are filled with life energy, with spirit, with love. As Shakespeare wrote, "O spirit of love, the spirit which heals." It is the spirit pervading the mind and body which is the healing force within us. When we are diseased, there will be an imbalance of Chi, of life energy, of spirit, affecting a specific acupuncture meridian, leading to particular psychological and physical problems and ultimately to disease. In this book you will learn how to overcome these energy imbalances and reactivate the life energy.

Our English word spirit comes from the Latin *spirare*, to breathe. The Latin word *spiritus* means breath, breath of a god, inspiration, breath of life, the soul. There would appear to be a primary root, what you might call an *sp* root, from which so many words relating to spirit have derived—spread, spray, spatter, spittle, spume, spit, spurt, sparse, sprinkle, spring, spry, disperse, esprit, spiratic, spray, sprinkle, spur, sputter, spirtle, splutter, split, sperm, speech, inspiration, aspiration, respiration, and many others. We see clearly in spit, spark, sperm, and speech, the prevailing underlying idea of the movement of organic, living matter by a breath-like expulsory act to a new site where it may grow and develop. Water springs from the ground and gives forth life. A spark is struck and starts a fire where it lands. A seed sprouts. Sperm are released and create new life, as may our speech. The spirit is the vital principle of life itself which by breathing life into us causes us to live and grow and love.

The Research procedure involves the accurate testing of the strength of an indicator muscle to assess the effects of nearly all stimuli—physical or psychological, internal or external—on the human body. It is basically a test of life energy, and can be used to gauge the relative functioning of the acupuncture meridians. Each acupuncture meridian is associated with specific muscles of facial expression, gesture, and vocalisation.[4] Most importantly for our present purposes, each meridian is also associated with a specific negative and a specific positive emotional state. Thus, through implementing this testing technique, it is possible to determine which emotional states are most affecting each of us, both mentally and physically, at any given time. We have found that, by bringing this to the person's attention and by using imagery techniques, the changes that can be produced are immediate and immediately apparent.

Five of the primary tenets upon which our approach to positive health rest recognise:

1. *the critical importance of the reduction of stress* and the concomitant emotional attitudes. Disease is seen as arising from stress that causes a general reduction in life energy and specific energy imbalances throughout the body.
2. the essential role of primary prevention—prevention *before* pathological change, either mental or physical. At this early stage the energy imbalances may be described as fluid or dynamic and readily amenable to correction. If the stress is prevented, if the mental attitudes are changed, then primary prevention will be operant and disease will not occur.
3. the individual's responsibility for taking charge of one's own health, and one's own way through life. In this context the role of the so-called doctor is that of teacher—to explain and to help the individual to see exactly what he is doing to lower his own healing energies. The individual has superimposed maladaptive behavioural patterns upon himself which have pulled him away from his natural, "normal" state, and he must recognise and alter them.
4. *that great healing forces exist within us* and in nature to enable repair to occur once the stress is reduced and the negative attitudes are corrected. It is recognised that natural methods are essential since unnatural methods often diminish life energy. While these unnatural methods may provide symptomatic relief, they ultimately lower the life energy, retard the true healing process, and do nothing to correct the stress and the attitudinal problems that are at the base of the disease patterns.
5. *that most problems begin at an energy level.* The first physical manifestation of imbalance within the body is at an energy level and corrections can be made at this level. On top of this are the metabolic, structural, and nutritional problems that also require attention.

From these five tenets we can see how disease begins. The specific negative emotional attitudes that we harbour give rise to stress. Stress, in turn, causes a reduction of life energy and energy imbalances which ultimately lead to disease. The disease did not just "appear" from nowhere. It actually began at an energy level.

For example, suppose that someone has a predominant emotional attitude of unhappiness. (I will give an exact definition of this emotional state later.) In other words, whenever this person is placed in a stressful situation, he will tend to react by becoming unhappy.

Now, if this emotional state continues, there will be a breakdown of the harmonious functioning of his cerebral hemispheres—that is, his body will be under stress. He will therefore be both physically and psychologically unable to cope with the stress as well as he could if that emotional attitude did not exist. Finally, the stress on his body will lead to a diminution of energy in the specific acupuncture meridian that relates to unhappiness. This meridian, as you will soon learn to test, is the liver meridian.

I am not suggesting that all liver disease is caused by unhappiness. But I am stating that in most cases of liver disease we do find impairment of the liver meridian as well as the specific emotional state of unhappiness. More importantly, I am proposing that if we can instantly correct the emotional state of unhappiness—as we can—we will function better at all times, we will not be stressed, and we will not interfere with the energy flow in the liver meridian. By preventing the stress, we will thus prevent energy impairment in the liver itself, which may ultimately have led to liver disease.

By applying what you have learned, you will be able to find out specifically how to eliminate or at least reduce the effects on you of the trouble spots in your life—those factors that are lowering your vital life energy day after day.

Remember, *it is not normal to get sick*, but unfortunately it is very common. Gradually people begin to expect poor health. They take out insurance policies in anticipation of a heart attack, arthritis, diabetes, or cancer that they feel is inevitable.

One very striking example of the way in which "normal" and "average" have become confused is apparent to me every time I look at a lab report detailing certain findings, such as the serum cholesterol level. Just a few years ago the acceptable range of this measure was 150-220 mgm percent. Then it became 150-250. Now it is 150-300. Imagine my dismay when I heard of a doctor telling his patient, "Well, your cholesterol is two-ninety, but don't worry. It's normal now." A few years ago it would not have been considered normal. As the level of serum cholesterol for the general population continues to increase, the accepted upper limit also increases. This does not mean that suddenly it is "normal" to have a cholesterol measure of, say, 285. It means only that it is becoming average. What does this say about our overall level of health?

Many people today tend to view disease as some foreign assault that suddenly "attacks" us almost without reason. We speak of a heart *attack,* or of being *stricken* with pneumonia or cancer. We find it very hard to realise that we create our own diseases—that a disease, when it occurs, is a result of our whole style and pattern of life. Everything we have inhaled, eaten, done or not done, and thought or not thought over all the years of our lives culminates in the illness. So, far from feeling as if we were just walking down the street minding our own business when suddenly a falling piece of masonry hits us on the head, we must recognise that most disease is of our own doing. Certainly some of the more virulent and dangerous elements in our environment that are now assaulting us are not of our own particular doing. But even there, to some extent, if we were to raise our life energy through positive health practices, we could prevent at least some if not most of the deleterious effects.

The first stage in prevention is to assume responsibility for ourselves and to accept our part in whatever happens to us. If we are in an accident, then we must ask at what level we were actually responsible for that accident. In the Australian army, no matter how innocent a driver would be found in civilian court, the army held him negligent for having become involved in that accident. He was deemed negligent for not having driven more defensively, for not having thought, in essence, more "preventively."

Thus whenever I or my patients and students become sick, I ask, and I suggest that they ask, "What have I done to produce this? What imbalances have I produced in the energy systems throughout my body that ultimately have manifested themselves in this physical disease?" Of course it may take many years for a physical disease to manifest itself. In all the time preceding this manifestation, the patterns are being formed in the same way as patterns of our future careers are laid down in our early years of schooling—which children shall have further academic education, which shall attend technical school, and so on. As we are thus *streamed* through life in terms of our employment, so we also have streams throughout life in terms of the diseases that we are likely to develop. These patterns of predisposition to disease are a result of specific energy imbalances in specific acupuncture meridian systems throughout the body.

The precipitating factor causing the initial energy imbalance will always be stress, physical or mental. The first result of that stress will always be a reduction of life energy. Coincidental with this, a specific negative emotional attitude will be created. It may be that of unhappiness, depression, anger, or any of the others that you will find described in later chapters. Each of these emotional attitudes relates to a specific acupuncture energy channel, or meridian, in the body, tending to cause an imbalance of life energy in the organs subserved by each meridian. (Remember that each meridian serves one or more organs and is called by the name of the organs. Hence we have names such as spleen meridian, bladder meridian, and so forth.)

If these negative emotional attitudes persist, the energy imbalances in the associated meridian(s) will persist and ultimately lead to disease. Let me give you a specific example. In my years in psychiatry and psychosomatic medicine, I found, as many other psychiatrists and cardiologists have found, that cardiac patients have great difficulty in dealing with anger. This is so before they have the heart attack and is more pronounced after the heart attack, when many of them fear that to become overtly angry could precipitate another heart attack. I remember one patient who got married for the first time when he was in his forties. He married the widow of one of his best friends. He had promised his old army mate as he lay dying that he would look after his widow. She, as he well knew, had always been a difficult wife to his friend. Now she proceeded to be the same with him. She was constantly shouting at him, berating and ridiculing him, continually comparing him unfavourably with her first husband, criticising his subordinate position at work, condemning his sexual performance, and so forth. If he had known the phrase, he would have called her "a regular Xanthippe." [5]

I saw him only a few times before his heart attack. Whenever I tried to get him to see that underneath his very calm exterior he was very, very angry whenever he mentioned his wife, he would protest that he did not feel angry with her at all. Although he certainly had anger toward her surging through his body, he did not *feel* it. However, it was so obvious—in his white face and clenched knuckles, particularly whenever he talked about how she belittled his sexual performance, what she referred to as his "husbandry duties." The heart attack occurred shortly after one of her attacks on his sexuality. I next saw him some months later, when it was even more difficult for him to recognise his anger toward her. Whenever I tried to bring it up in our discussions no matter how subtly, he would make a movement with his head of both turning away and sort of nodding, half-saying yes and half-saying no, while simultaneously doing his best to dismiss it. He could not deal with his internal anger. When I pointed out to him how much his wife had mistreated him, he would say, "Well, Doc," with that flick of the head, "she's had a hard life and who am I to judge her?" or some equally ineffectual platitude.

It took quite a time in therapy before this man finally came to grips with his anger toward his wife. This was primarily because he was, of course, haunted by memories of his heart attack and fearful that he would have another. The memory of his heart attack—with him lying on the floor of a train clutching his chest in pain, staring up at all the passengers looking down at him from what seemed to be a very great height—was so fixed in his mind that he dared not ever face up to his anger. He feared he would precipitate another heart attack and he would have to relive that nightmare.

This story, with perhaps a few minor changes, could be told by any psychiatrist who has tried to work with cardiac cases.

The underlying specific emotional state in most if not all such cases is that of anger—chronic, ongoing, festering anger. This anger is often conscious, but also frequently unconscious—that is, not known to the patient. I say unconscious because he is so unable to deal with it that he represses it, pushes it down, out of his mind.

What we will find in most people who have cardiac problems is that one of the acupuncture meridians that constantly tests weak will be the heart meridian. This is not surprising. What is surprising is that whenever this meridian tests weak, if the patient then says, "I am not angry, I forgive," it will instantly be found that the meridian tests strong. If this affirmation is repeated often enough, with feeling, over a period of time, the heart meridian will cease to test weak, indicating that the energy has re-balanced and the body is now going about repairing any damage as best it can.

In people who do not seem to have cardiac problems it will also be found that if they say, "I am angry," then their heart meridian (which previously tested strong) will test weak. Thus all of us have a tendency to heart-meridian energy imbalances whenever we feel angry.

From the above example comes a very important finding. Just saying we are angry, or conversely, that we forgive, somehow creates within us a negative or positive emotional state and causes a change in the specific acupuncture meridian involved. The emotion of anger creates a negative energy imbalance in the heart meridian; merely by saying "I am angry" you can create a negative energy imbalance in that meridian. We must not underestimate the power of the word and its great potential for good, as we have demonstrated. Saying "I forgive" restores the heart meridian to its proper energy balance.

I do not mean to imply that any time someone's heart meridian tests weak it means he or she has heart disease or is going to have a coronary occlusion. What I am saying is that you will always find in such cases that there is the negative emotion of anger which is interfering with life energy, which is affecting the heart meridian and to some extent the heart, and which can be corrected by the appropriate affirmation. Should this energy imbalance, this unconscious emotional attitude of anger, persist for a long period of time, then it can lead, and often does lead, to cardiac disease. This is the basic premise of psychosomatic medicine.

Now we can see *how* the emotion leads to the heart disease—through the acupuncture system. We can also see how to prevent it. If we overcome our anger, which can be very simply accomplished as we will learn, then we will never hold the energy problems for long in the meridian, therefore we will not be predisposed to a heart attack.

This is what I mean by prevention. *By continually monitoring our meridian states, and instantly correcting, through the appropriate positive thought, any that are out of balance, we can keep our life energy high and balanced and thus prevent disease.* In this context I should point out again that the ancients knew psychosomatic medicine. As the Greeks knew that the life energy *(thymos)* was related to the thymus gland, so it was known that angry people were predisposed to heart disease.

There is a common origin through most of European civilisation in the history of the words *anger* and *angina*. This is true not only in the history of the word throughout our Indo-European civilisation, but also in terms of the history of the disease in the individual.

Having overcome the negative emotional states, you are in a position to practice true prevention. You will find that the thymus gland tests strong, that the life energy has been raised, and that the cerebral hemispheres are balanced in their functioning, thus allowing creativity. You are on the road to positive health—not just preventing yourself from being sick, but starting to be positively well.

For most of us this is the first time we really feel energy surging through our bodies. We begin to be alert, suddenly able to be creative in all our daily activities. The change is beautiful and gratifying. I have seen it so many times in patients and students, and it is a wondrous and inspiring experience when a patient who has been struggling with the handicap of cerebral imbalance, struggling with his formal education or struggling to solve his problems at work, or struggling with life in general, begins to experience this phenomenon. He becomes truly creative. He walks easily where before he stumbled. Life becomes exciting, full, rich, and manageable.

This is what we are trying to achieve. First we recognise the specific emotional states that are depleting our life energies, deactivating our thymus glands, and leading to cerebral hemisphere functional imbalances. We recognise that this makes it hard for us to solve our problems and creates other emotional imbalances, which then lead to specific energy imbalances in the acupuncture meridians supplying energy to all the organs and muscles of our bodies. If we correct these emotional imbalances early, we stay healthy. If we do not correct them, we sink into a state that is now considered normal but which is far from normal—the state of going from illness to illness, from operation to operation, living short, unproductive, uncreative, disease-ridden lives. None of this is normal. None of this is what was intended for us.

Our heritage is to lead long, healthy, happy, fully productive and creative lives. We must get away from the working model of disease and non-disease and create for ourselves a new health model in which illness as we now know it has no place. This we can do when our life energy is high and when the energy systems of our bodies are balanced. The easiest way to achieve this is to correct the specific emotional attitudes that are a result of stress and lead to energy imbalances throughout the body.

What we must now learn is how to identify and correct these emotional attitudes early.

Part 2

The Acupuncture Meridians

William Furtwangler is one of the great high-life energy conductors of all time. His music activates life energy and so do his musical gestures. Most people will test strong when looking at this photo.

Introduction to Acupuncture

Have you ever been curious about acupuncture? Have you ever wanted to explore it but were frightened by its complexities, its mystique—and by the needles? Remember that acupuncture does not require needles. This concept was begun by a mistranslation of the Chinese word by one of the first Western observers of the technique. The treatment is frequently carried out with needles, but they are not essential.

Acupuncture is the science and art of re-balancing the life energy (which the Chinese call the Chi) throughout the body—and now you can do it.

Acupuncture energy, the Chi, is probably electromagnetic in origin just as the life force itself probably is, although we cannot, of course, be sure of this. When the acupuncture energy is flowing strongly and freely throughout the body, we will find that the cerebral hemispheres will be balanced. Also we will find that the thymus will test strong because the thymus test is basically a test of how much acupuncture energy is coursing through the body at that time. This energy flows through the body in a definite pattern, entering through the lung meridian. The Chinese said that the Chi comes into the body as the breath. It then flows through the twelve paired channels called meridians and is, in a sense, collected in two midline meridians, one at the back and one at the front. That at the back is called the governing vessel and that at the front is called the conception vessel. The two meet when the lips touch.

The acupuncture meridians are named after the various organs of the body, which the Chinese recognised some thousands of years ago were energised by specific meridians.[1] If there is an energy problem or a physical problem with the stomach, for example, there will be an impairment of energy in the stomach meridian. The acupuncturist's task, in this case, whether he uses needles or other means, is to rebalance the energy in the stomach meridian so that the healing energy of the body can correct the problem and then, by continually supplying energy as needed to the area, enable the stomach to go about performing its everyday task of digestion. Whenever there is an energy imbalance in the meridian serving an organ, it means that the organ's physiological function is impaired, which may ultimately lead to physical disease in the specific organ.

Through our research we have discovered that each meridian also has *a specific emotional attitude, positive and negative, related to it.* For example, in the case of the stomach meridian, the negative emotional attitudes, those that can reduce the energy in the meridian and therefore in the organ and tend to lead to the organ's impaired functioning, are those of disappointment, disgust, and greed. Later, when we come to consider the stomach meridian in more detail, you will learn exactly what these emotional states are and why it is so appropriate and inevitable that they relate to the stomach and to the stomach meridian. The positive emotional state that optimises the performance of the stomach meridian, that maximises the positive energy in that meridian and therefore the functioning of the organ, is the state of contentment.

Just as we have twelve sets of organ meridians, we have twelve psychological meridian types, positive and negative. And as I have stated previously, each is basically controlled by the deep feelings of love or fear and hate that are the properties of the controller of all the acupuncture energy, the thymus gland.

Further, six of the sets of meridians, and therefore six personality types, are related to the left cerebral hemisphere, and six to the right cerebral hemisphere. A person who has, say, left-hemisphere dominance, will have energy impairment in the group of meridians related to the left hemisphere. So, to arrive at an understanding of the personality types we will now discuss at length, we first needed to understand the thymus gland, the master controller of all our emotions and all our acupuncture energy, as well as the functions of the hemispheres. To understand the functions of each cerebral hemisphere was also essential because each hemisphere regulates and is regulated by six sets of meridians and six sets of emotional states.

Psychosomatic Illness and Health

We are beginning to understand the origin of psychosomatic illness. Suppose we are subjected to a specific negative emotional state. This will cause a weakening of thymus activity, a general impairment of life energy, as well as a specific impairment of energy in the particular meridian relating to that specific emotional state. If that emotional state persists long enough, the associated meridian will remain impaired and the impaired physiology of the organ could lead to disease. Thus, to continue with our example of stomach-meridian energy imbalance, we could say that should the negative emotional attitudes of disappointment or disgust persist long enough, it could lead to gastritis or perhaps to a gastric ulcer. This would be the specific emotional state that relates to these stomach-meridian energy problems. We could likewise say that if the person always was contented, he should be almost invulnerable to gastritis or a gastric ulcer.

What about somato-psychic illness? What about the emotional state induced by a physical illness? For example, suppose someone has suffered a trauma to the stomach. The stomach meridian will be impaired, and this will then provoke the specific emotional state of disappointment, greed, or disgust. The way to overcome this somato-psychic component of the physical illness would be to encourage the person to feel contented. All this will become more obvious in the section devoted to the stomach meridian.

If we can determine which meridian is impaired, we will know the particular negative emotional attitude operant at that moment. How do we test the meridians? In the chart, we have designated the meridian test points. These points have been used for several thousand years in acupuncture treatments. In order to test the meridian for an energy imbalance, first test the indicator muscle in the clear. Then while test-touching a point and re-testing the indicator muscle, you may detect a meridian energy imbalance.

If your subject's thymus tests weak, then you will almost always find a meridian imbalance. For example, if the subject places one or two fingers midway between his umbilicus and the point where the ribs come together in the midline at the front of the body and his indicator muscle tests weak, this indicates a stomach meridian imbalance, and it gives us the indication that the predominant emotional state affecting him at that moment is one of disappointment, disgust, or greed.

Can we prove this? Yes, and very simply. If your subject tested weak at the stomach meridian test point as described above, ask him to say, preferably aloud, "I am content." He will test strong.[2] To look at this from the other direction, suppose your subject's stomach meridian test point does not test weak. Ask him to say, while continuing to touch the test point, "I am greedy, I am disappointed, I am disgusted." Now you will find that these, and only these, statements will cause his stomach meridian point to test weak. The remarkable power of these precise affirmations cannot be overemphasised.

This test is simple to perform and it can be done by anyone. However, it requires experience and practice to do the testing reliably and accurately, and variables must be controlled. Through its use, we can discover which of our body organs are functioning under stress, the particular emotional attitudes affecting us at the time, and how to correct them. In the process of learning this test technique, we have discovered more than anyone practicing psychosomatic medicine has been able to determine with the myriad of complicated laboratory procedures at his disposal—that is, specifically which emotional states are related to which organic diseases.

Let me give you an example. The other day, I had a severe headache. I had no idea why I had it, but it was so severe that I decided to cancel my appointments for the day to stay in bed. Before doing that I had my wife test my meridians. We discovered that my thyroid meridian was testing weak. I then recognised that, although I didn't actually feel it, I was depressed. So I said the positive affirmations for the thyroid meridian, thinking clearly about what the words meant as I said them several times: "I am light and buoyant." My headache vanished instantly, and I got up and completed a full day's work without any recurrence. I could mention hundreds of examples such as this, and in the following chapter we will discuss a few more in detail.

Another common example occurs in the late afternoon when many people start to feel tired. This time is when their blood sugar drops—what we call the "hypoglycaemia hour."[3] On testing at this time we often find that the spleen meridian controlling the pancreas, which regulates blood sugar, tests weak. If the subject says the positive affirmation for the spleen meridian, "I have faith and confidence in my future," the spleen meridian weakness disappears. Often these people report that they no longer feel tired. In fact, after using this affirmation, most feel energised.

Through the use of this simple test, *you can demonstrate to yourself the power of thought and the power of the word to create great energy changes throughout the body.* You have already learned that, in extreme, thoughts can cure us and thoughts can kill us. You have learned what we have tried so hard to teach in psychiatry and what now is so easy to demonstrate. Thoughts have power. Hence good psychiatry, and all techniques that reduce stress, overcome negative emotional attitudes, really can save our lives. This is the ultimate working point. Our positive thoughts are our greatest form of prevention.

As you examine the diagram of the acupuncture test points, you will see that six of the test points are represented just once and are in the midline of the body, whereas six of the test points are on each side and thus are represented twice. These we call, respectively, the "midline" and the "bilateral" test points.[4]

When your subject is left-hemisphere dominant, one at the midline meridians will test weak, but none of the bilateral points will test weak. Conversely, if the subject tests right-hemisphere dominant, then one of the bilateral points will test weak, but none of the midline meridian test points will be weak. This is because each hemisphere controls six sets of meridians.

To review: Whenever we are subjected to any form of stress, there will be a disturbance of the life energy such that the thymus will be deactivated and one hemisphere will become dominant. A specific meridian that is controlled by the dominant hemisphere will also be affected. This meridian will have specific negative and positive personality characteristics. We can overcome the effect of the stress by balancing the hemispheres or by activating the thymus, or by saying or thinking the specific positive emotional attitude affirmations for the involved meridian. *This is the wonder of the human mind and body.*

This is the manner in which the surging forces, the waves, of Chi, of life energy, flow through us. And this is the way we can at all times attempt to rise above the stresses to which we are constantly subjected, which threaten to weaken us and lead to disease. This is our way of prevention. And it can be done with our thoughts and our words. This is the power of the mind to control the energy of the body. This is the greatest form of psychological care, and each of us can do it for ourselves. This, as I promised at the outset, is the emancipation of the psychiatry patient. This is what you can do for yourself.

Psychiatry, unfortunately, has become obsessed with determining *why* we are troubled in the ways that we are. Here we don't need to concern ourselves with the *why*. All we need to do is find out *what* is the negative emotional attitude affecting us and then to transmute it instantly through our will to be well into its positive opposite. This is instant transmutational psychiatry—the way that you can, day by day, keep yourself well, mentally and physically. This is the way to psychosomatic health.

The Meridians and Their Emotions

In this chapter our goal is to arrive at the true meaning of the positive and negative emotional states associated with each meridian. It is very important for several reasons that we be specific about these emotional states. The first reason is so that we will be talking about the same quality. One of the biggest problems in any discussion of the emotional states is that frequently everyone does not mean the same thing when they talk about depression, for example, or frustration, gratitude, or contentment. We all think we mean the same thing, but we may not.[1]

Then, too, we have discovered that the better we know the word and its history and its usage's throughout time, the better we understand the emotional state that accompanies it. The better we know the emotional states, the better we will be able to correct our negative attitudes and to balance our meridian energy.

In addition, it is important that we be specific so that we can differentiate between apparently similar emotions, such as depression and unhappiness. Although these are often used interchangeably in describing how we feel, they do in fact affect different meridians, and it is important to distinguish between them. An examination of their origin and meaning helps make all this clearer. (Incidentally, this is the first time, to my knowledge, that all these common positive and negative emotional states have been so discussed—not only in terms of the meridians, but also in terms of their etymology and usage over the years.)

In the course of our investigation, we frequently go back to the hypothetical Indo-European roots of the words (referred to as the I-E root). It is believed that most words in the English language have come from such an origin, of which Sanskrit is a late form, and the only form of which we have much knowledge. By getting back to these root words, we can often understand a great deal more about the words and thus the emotional states.[2]

History in a sense persists in our unconscious. The historical origin of the word in the past lives on in our unconscious as our deep understanding, our gestalt of the word. The history of the word is thus deeply rooted and embedded in our present-day unconscious.

As you read these etymologies, keep in mind that they are physical interpretations of the words. In the primitive word the physical and the abstract were combined as they are in a primitive language today. Over the years we have, with our reasoning intelligence, tended to remove the right-brain poetic qualities of the words, while concentrating on the more physical characteristics. Owen Barfield has pointed out that the earliest elementary meanings carried the poetic, metaphorical qualities along with the physical, and that later these qualities became separated.[3] How this happened will be apparent as we examine the specific emotional states that follow.

For each meridian I will delineate the predominant negative and positive emotions. As you will see, there will be many apparently separate emotional states connected with each meridian. We know that all these apparently different emotional states are in fact related because they involve the same meridian on testing.

With each meridian type, a photographic representation will be given. You will find that when you look at the picture and test the appropriate meridian, it will test weak, demonstrating that it is the meridian that is being affected. But if at the same time you say the specific positive affirmation for that meridian, the negative effect will be overcome.[4]

It is important that the positive affirmation always be stated positively. You do not say, for example, "I am not depressed," but rather, "I am light and buoyant." It is not the *absence* of the negative that we want, but the *presence* of the positive.

I am not in any way advocating the techniques in this book as the primary treatment of any severe physical illness. But I am suggesting that there is usually an emotional component in serious physical illness that can be specifically helped by these techniques. Especially when the illness is minor, or when it still exists as an energy problem before there is grossly disturbed physiology in any way, then what I am advocating can be truly preventive and can then lead to positive health.

"Bilateral" Meridians

The meridians whose test points are bilaterally represented:

Lung
Liver
Gall Bladder
Spleen
Kidney
Large Intestine

One of these meridians will test weak when the subject is right hemisphere dominant.

Lung Meridian

The meridian of humility

Tolerance	Lung
Intolerance	

Negative Emotions:	Disdain
	Scorn
	Contempt
	Haughtiness
	False Pride
	Intolerance
	Prejudice
Positive Affirmations:	I am humble.
	I am tolerant.
	I am modest.

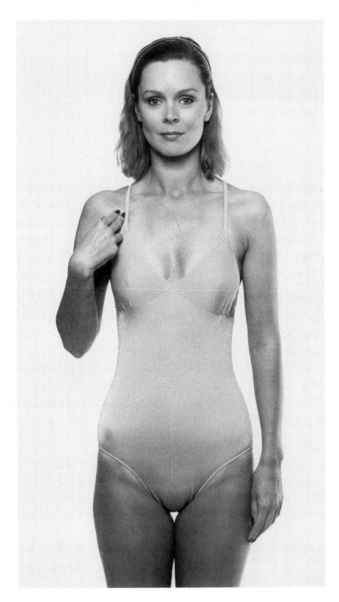

The test point for the lung meridian. In the first intercostal space on the anterior paraxillary line.

Test Image: You are with someone who you feel is
                   very silly or ignorant. You feel much
                   smarter and you are very aware of the
                   contrast between your genius and his
                   or her stupidity, and you feel superior.

"Blessed are the meek: for they shall inherit the earth."
                                        — *Matthew 5:5*

We will commence with the lung meridian because, as previously mentioned, the Chinese regarded the life energy, the Chi,
as being derived from the breath and entering the body through
the lung meridian and then passing into the other meridians.
They regarded the lung meridian as the prime meridian. The lung
meridian is that which is most involved in normal and abnormal
early childhood development.

With each meridian personality type, I will give you an instance
(test image) to think on which will activate the associated negative
emotional attitude. Then you can prove for yourself that these
emotional states do indeed relate to these specific meridians. For
example, test your subject's lung meridian test point and it should
be strong. Now have your subject think of and strongly visualise
being with someone who he feels is silly and ignorant. The subject
feels much smarter and is very aware of the contrast between his
own genius and the other person's stupidity. His lung meridian
will test weak. This is the specific negative emotional state associated with the lung meridian.

The negative words relating to the lung meridian all have to do
with feeling superior to or looking down on another person. In
fact, one of the negative gestures that relates to the lung meridian
is a tilting of the head backward, a "looking down the nose" with
a feeling of scorn, and frequently, a wrinkling up of the nose, as if
one had smelled something bad. The image of this I always have
in mind is of the English upper-class snob.

The negative emotional attitudes associated with the lung meridian, then, are disdain, scorn, contempt, haughtiness, false pride,
intolerance, and prejudice. We could say in many cases that people
who have lung-meridian energy problems are those whose chests
are "puffed out with pride." "Haughty" is often applied to those
who imagine themselves as being higher than or superior to
others. We could call the lung meridian "the meridian of judge-

Most people will test weak for the lung meridian when looking at this photo. Saying the positive affirmation for the lung meridian will overcome the weakness.

ment of others in relation to self", or the meridian of humility. Now these are very powerful words, and it may offend you somewhat to find that your lung meridian tests weak. It may seem particularly distasteful to you that anyone, especially you, could be harbouring such negative qualities. Rest assured, though, we all do at one time or another. At some point in testing any person, we are going to find these feelings.

Remember, too, we are speaking of degrees. If your lung meridian tests weak, it does not mean that you are contemptuous or scornful. It simply means that you have a tendency to feel this way at the particular time of testing. If we find that we have a lung meridian weakness on testing, we should acknowledge this, and then turn it around, transmuting it into the positive feeling.

Transmutation is surrendering the negative state and turning it around into the positive—instantly, harmlessly, inexpensively, and without outside intervention. To do this, you do not need a psychiatrist. You just need to have the will and desire to give up the negative and come forward into the positive.

Disdain

Disdain is that "feeling entertained toward that which one thinks unworthy of notice or beneath one's dignity; scorn, contempt."[5] Lindley Murray wrote, "Haughtiness is founded on the high opinion we entertain of ourselves; disdain, on the low opinion we have of others."

Each meridian's related positive and negative emotional states are like a continuum, going from one extreme to the other. We can see in Murray the idea of highness and lowness in our opinion of others in relationship to ourselves. This highness and lowness is the continuum of the emotional state of the lung meridian. The lung meridian is a continuum of what we might call superiority/inferiority.

(Dis)dain is derived from the primitive root *dek*, which meant to take or accept. It is also related to several Latin roots, *decere*, from which we get the word *decent;* dignus, which gave rise to the word *deign*, meaning to think worthy; and dedignore, which meant to think unworthy.

Scorn

Scorn comes from the Latin *cornu*, a horn, and it means literally to deprive of one's horns, and thus to mock, to humiliate. The horns have long been a symbol of power and fertility. To be dehorned, to be scorned, is to suffer gross humiliation. Thus we get the saying, "To scorn a thing, as a dog scorns tripe."

Shakespeare in *Twelfth Night* wrote,

> Oh, what a deal of scorn looks beautiful
> In the contempt and anger of his lip!

Contempt

Contempt has been defined as "the holding or treating as of a little account, or as vile and worthless." Thus Thomas Hobbes said, "Contempt, is when a man thinks another of little worth in comparison to himself." Contempt has also been called bitter scorn. It comes from the Latin *cum*, meaning wholly, and *temnere*, to despise, and so means to wholly despise. It is probably related to the Greek *temnein*, to cut, and perhaps has a similar unconscious meaning as scorn. Indeed, Johnson defined contempt as "the act of despising others; slight regard; scorn."

The idea of the attacking, cutting, destructive quality of contempt is well shown in the expression, "Contempt pierces even through the shell of the tortoise."

Haughtiness

"Before destruction the heart of man is haughty, and before honour is humility." Proverbs 18:12

Haughtiness obviously relates to highness, again with the idea of being superior, of having one's nose in the air. When Richard II was deposed, Northumberland contemptuously addressed him as "Lord." Richard angrily replied, "No Lord of thine, thou haught insulting man."

Haughty is derived from the French *haut*, meaning high, which is derived from the Latin *altum*, from which we get *altitude*. Haughty means to be high in one's own estimation; lofty and disdainful in feeling or demeanour; proud, arrogant, supercilious, elevated.

Haughtiness beautifully describes the idea of the lung meridian characteristic of "nose up in the air," rising up above others, feeling oneself to be higher and superior to others. (Hence Crashaw's, "Down, down, proud sense."[6] Interestingly, the origin of *altus* is from the Latin *alere*, meaning to nourish—and well-nourished implies growing, becoming tall. This is the origin of *alimentary*.

False Pride

Buck notes that in many Indo-European languages, several of the words for *pride* imply over or high, "thus connoting superiority of spirit or mind."[7] In Shakespeare's *Henry VIII* we read "my high-blown pride." True pride, the true feeling of one's own self-worth and accomplishment, is a very valuable and essential state, as we shall see when we come to consider the large-intestine meridian and associated emotional states. But false and overbearing pride is a negative emotion weakening the lung meridian. (Isaiah 2:11 — "The lofty looks of man shall be humbled, and the haughtiness of men shall be bowed down.")

Hubris is "overbearing pride; arrogance," and interestingly was derived from the hypothetical Indo-European root *ud*, meaning "up," which is most apt when we think of the proud person with his nose up in the air. The *New Encyclopedia Britannica* speaks of "impious disregard of the limits governing men's actions in an orderly universe ... and in Greek tragedy it is usually the basic flaw of the tragic hero."[8] The heart of the traditional Greek religion and Greek tragedy, Gilbert Murray suggests, is "the story of *Pride and Punishment*."[9] Melanie Klein refers to Murray's definition, "the typical sin which all things, so far as they have life, commit is in poetry *Hubris*, a word generally translated 'insolence' or 'pride' ... Hubris grasps at more, bursts bounds and breaks the order; it is followed by Dike, Justice, which re-establishes them. This rhythm—Hubris–Dike, Pride and its fall, Sin and Chastisement—is the commonest burden of those philosophical lyrics which are characteristic of Greek tragedy."[10]

The Greek scholar, E. R. Dodds, defines hubris as "arrogance in word or deed or even thought ... the 'primal evil,' the sin whose wages is death."[11] Adrian Stokes defines hubris as "the great sin of pride, which comes about by believing oneself to be the god, by scorning the laws of gods and men."[12]

The primary meridian is the lung meridian, and it is here that we will find the most deeply rooted disturbances—those present in our earliest days and the most all-pervading influences throughout our lives. The Greek religion was based on the overcoming of pride, a problem of the primary meridian, the lung meridian. This also became the basis of Greek tragedy. Perhaps the Greeks understood human nature even better than Shakespeare.

Intolerance

"Judge not that ye be not judged." — Matthew 7:1

From the I-E root *tel*, meaning to lift or support and to weigh, we get the idea of measuring weights, thus implying money and payment, hence the related English word *toll*.

The verb from which *intolerance* was derived was *tolerare*, meaning to bear or to endure. We speak today of being able to tolerate the pain, for example.

We say a tolerant person is one who bears with our imperfections and hopes that we will bear with his. On the other hand, an intolerant person is one who feels that he has no imperfections and cannot bear those of others. Again, the basic attitude of intolerance is one of superiority, or what has been called hateful superiority.

I recall a patient who suffered from severe asthma for many years. He was a very small man who always seemed to have his nose up in the air, looking down at people. He had what was described as a "Napoleon complex." He was blustery and intolerant of anyone's mistakes, and for this reason his secretaries were continually resigning. He was argumentative and tolerated imperfection very badly indeed. He continually tested weak at the lung meridian test point. It was a difficult task to gently point out to him what this meridian weakness implied. Eventually he got the message and he began saying the appropriate affirmation regularly. Surprisingly for him and for me, his asthma attacks stopped. He changed; he stopped looking down his nose at people, both physically and metaphorically. He became a pleasant, tolerant, and much more likeable person.

Read how the Psalmist has summed up the negative emotional states related to the lung meridian: "Our soul is exceedingly filled with the scorning of those that are at ease, and with the contempt of the proud." Psalm 123:4

Prejudice

Prejudice is a prejudgment, a preconceived opinion. It is a bias usually, although not necessarily, against a person or thing. Prejudice means that one's mind is made up beforehand. Rather than judging an individual truly on his own merits and then reaching a decision, someone who is prejudiced makes a decision based on race or religion or education, or the like. The decision is made before the faculties of reason are invoked. The *Oxford English Dictionary* defines it as a "preconceived, unreasonable opinion, bias, or leaning; a judgement formed before due examination or consideration" of the facts. We might call prejudice a mental set, a rigid attitude which exists before enough data are available to exercise reason and arrive at a considered opinion.

It will be found that when there is prejudice there will be a weakness of the lung meridian on testing. In fact, it is possible to use this test to find out a person's potential for prejudice. For example, print on a plain piece of paper a neutral name such as "Robert Jones." (If your subject happens to know someone by that name, then use a similar name which he does not associate with a particular person.) Have the subject look at the name on the piece of paper and he should test strong. Now, under "Robert Jones," write the word, "Banker." Your subject will most likely test strong. If your subject has a potential lung meridian weakness, he may test weak for "Roberta Jones, Banker."

Your subject may test weak in the clear or just at the lung meridian test point. In either case the basic meridian involved is the lung meridian. By reinforcing the meridian with the positive affirmation, "I am humble," he will now test strong when he looks at the sign, "Roberta Jones, Banker," and he is on the way to overcoming his prejudice.

There are many other prejudices for which you can test. Of course, not all prejudices are gender-oriented. For example, most people test weak when looking at the name, "Robert Jones, Psychiatrist." Even other psychiatrists often test weak, indicating the widespread prejudice involved. Many people have unconscious prejudices against the handicapped, for example. Test for yourself and discover your own prejudices. In every case, the weakness found on testing will be overcome by the affirmation, "I am humble."

The positive emotional attributes of the lung meridian are tolerance, humility, and modesty. Perhaps the "best," and the one that has been found most effective in clinical practice besides tolerance, is humility.

Humility

"Better it is to be of an humble spirit with the lowly, than to divide the spoil with the proud." Proverbs 16:19

Humility has been defined as meekness, the opposite of pride or haughtiness. The primitive Sanskrit word from which *humble* is derived means earth, and this gives rise to the Old English word *guma*, meaning a man. In Latin, the word for earth is *humus*—an expression we use in gardening even today. Hence humility reminds us of our origins from the earth. We recognise and accept these origins and we are humble. It is difficult to feel superior to others if we recognise that we are all from the earth.

Whateley said, "That is true humility, to have a meane esteeme of himselfe out of a true apprehension of God's greatnesse."[13]

There is a bird called "the Humility," so named because "it seldom mounts high in the air." Perhaps this best sums it up. The negative attributes of the lung meridian arise when we "mount high in the air," our noses up in the air, when we feel proud and superior and contemptuous of those whom we judge to be below us. But the positive attributes of humility and tolerance come with our recognition of our imperfections, the realisation that we are not to judge others by our own standards, and an understanding of our own places in life.

Modesty

Another positive affirmation for the lung meridian is, "I am modest." Modesty is "having or showing a moderate estimation of one's own talents, abilities, and value." It comes from the I-E root *med* which means to take measures. This became in Latin *modus*, a measure, from which was derived in Latin *modestus*, meaning modest, within bounds or measure.

Thus Samuel Butler wrote, "Nothing renders Men modest, but

a just Knowledge how to compare themselves with others." Modesty illustrates and embodies the positive qualities of the lung meridian, neither undervaluing ourselves nor overvaluing ourselves or our attributes in relationship to others—seeing ourselves fairly and justly and seeing our own abilities within bounds, having a reasonable comprehension of our own worth and value. Modesty is the opposite of false pride.

Liver Meridian

The meridian of happiness

Happiness	Liver
Unhappiness	

Negative Emotion: Unhappiness
Positive Affirmations: I am happy.
                        I have good fortune.
                        I am cheerful.

Test Image: You are very unhappy because your lover
                       has left you. Everything would be perfect
                       if only he would come back to you.

Happiness and Unhappiness

The predominant emotions for the liver meridian are happiness and unhappiness.

Let us examine some of the expressions and origins of the word *happy*. You will be reminded, as I was when I first came across them, of the successful gambler. For example, happiness is defined as luck, or good fortune, or the state of prosperity. The original root meant to succeed. This gave rise to the word in Old Norse, *happ*, which was chance or good luck. From this we got our English word *happy*, via the Old English word *hap*, which in its original sense meant good luck. Johnson defines happiness as "Good luck, good fortune, lucky, successful, fortunate." Hence the phrase *happy-go-*

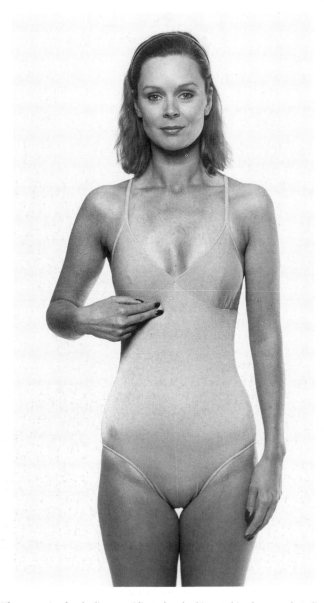

The test point for the liver meridian when looking at this photograph. In line with the nipple at about the costal border, usually just above it.

Most people will test weak for the liver meridian when looking at this photo. Saying the positive affirmation for the liver meridian will overcome the weakness.

lucky. We feel happy when fortune has smiled on us—when the gods smile on us, when those who control our destiny, be it good fortune, the gods, our parents, lady luck, or the government, are benevolent. When these external benefactors smile on us, we feel happy. Conversely, when we feel that those who are in a position to give to us withhold from us instead, then we feel *unhappy*.

We read in Psalm 144:15, "Happy is that people, that is in such a case: yea, happy is that people, whose God is the Lord."

And in the context of happiness as feeling smiled upon by the gods, Catullus wrote, "What is given by the gods more desirable than a happy hour."

It is important that we distinguish between depression and unhappiness. There is considerable confusion in psychiatry regarding the state of depression. Depression has now become quite acceptable because we have antidepressant drugs. On the other hand unhappiness is not acceptable and even has a rather childish or epithetical connotation about it that depression does not have. Thus a great many people who are called "depressed" are really not depressed at all—they are unhappy. The depressed person feels that he is heavy, he is down, he is literally de-pressed. He also feels that it is his fault and his responsibility to get himself out of this situation, if it can be done, which he usually doubts. "Genuine" suicide attempts usually come out of depression, but the attempt that is not "genuine" is usually a product of unhappiness and a wish to have others do more for him.

The unhappy person feels that the fault always lies with someone else: if only his wife had done such and such, then he would not be bankrupt. If only the government would do more for him, then he would be a success. If only lady luck had smiled on him, he would have made a fortune at gambling. If only God had answered his prayers. With the state of unhappiness there is always the feeling that if only the powers that be (which in our psyche always comes down to our parents) had given me more, I would now be perfect, I would now be happy. Joseph Ratner wrote, "If we are born under a lucky star, and are fortunate and happy lovers of the ideal, the ecstasy of the mystic's beatific vision is ours."[14]

Those who continually complain that they are not given enough are unhappy. You constantly hear that everything would be fine *if only* they were given more. These are the unhappy people. They are not depressed. It is in this state that an alcoholic will turn to the bottle, feeling that his happiness can be given to him through the bottle.[15] But he is not a baby any more. He must find his own goals in life, he must find his own homing thought. He must activate his will to be well, roll up his sleeves and find what he needs for himself He will not gain if he stays back in a state of unhappiness and expects to have "it" given to him.

So much of our present-day social and political thinking and advertising plays into the state of unhappiness. We have been led to believe that the government will provide us with all we need, or that the corporation for which we work will assume this responsibility to provide, or that big business itself will take care of us. So we abdicate our responsibility for our own fulfilment and expect these external, godlike, fortune-distributing institutions to supply our needs. And we become unhappy when this does not occur. When the next election comes we turn to another candidate. We reject the previous candidate and elect a new one, who again has promised to do everything he can for us, and whom we know we will reject in a few years' time—because he has no more satisfied our unhappiness than the previous elected official.

Advertising plays into our unhappiness almost constantly, making us aware of what we do not have and implying that the institution, the company, the advertiser, will supply us with happiness with their largess. All we have to do is pay for it. The implication is that we are gaining more than just goods in exchange for our money. We believe the answer lies in possessing the product—an external solution to an internal problem. Thus we find, for example, that when a shopping mall is built, part of the basic design, part of its gestalt, is that it was not created to be a place where you will exchange money for goods but rather is a place of fun, of happiness.

Yet honourable advertising can actually strengthen, and raise your life energy. Unfortunately, most advertising weakens us. It is quite possible for advertising to be honourable and to work to the advantage of society while at the same time encouraging the usage of the product being advertised. Wholesome advertising could actually energise us.

Perhaps it is significant that the liver is called just that. Many physicians have stated that the proper functioning of the liver is absolutely essential for good health, bearing in mind the multiple functions that the liver performs. I think the quotation of Spencer is appropriate here: "Happiness is added Life, and the giver of Life!" As the founder of the International Academy of Preventive

Medicine, Dr. R. 0. Brennan, has remarked many times, "To have a long life, you must be a liver lover." To this I would add, "And you must be happy."

At the beginning of this book I said that the fact that my patients did not get better made me unhappy. This was because I recognised that they were not doing as well as they should, and I felt I had done everything I possibly could do to help them be completely well. If only I had been given more assistance; if only I had been taught better. If only the hospital had done a better job; if only the medical insurance agencies would leave the patients alone; if only the relatives would leave the patient alone. I kept looking for that extra source, that smiling of fortune from outside that was going to help me to achieve what I felt was beyond me to achieve.

Happiness goes with coming to grips with the fact that we must not rely on other people—that we are masters of our own fates. Only this way can we mature and develop from our position of dependence on our parents and others in society, particularly its institutions. Ultimately, through overcoming our unhappiness it is possible that we can develop our own correct relationship with fortune, with the gods, and with God. The concept of prayer today seems to be, "If only God would do more for me, if only He would provide more, then I would be happy. Therefore I will pray to Him that He will give me these things." The "if only someone would ..." is the complaint of the unhappy, dependent child, not of the independent, self-contained adult, striving toward his goal of personal evolution. An independent, self-sufficient course through life is what we require.

Cheer

Another emotional state closely related to happiness and thus to the liver meridian is cheerfulness, which has been defined as "gaiety; animation; happiness." Its origin is very interesting. The I-E root is *ker*, which the American Heritage Dictionary states is "horn, head; with derivatives referring to horned animals, horn-shaped objects, and projecting parts," from which we get such words as *unicorn, cornet, horn.* The extended root *keras* gives rise to such words as cervix (related to neck) and words to do with the head itself—cerebrum, cerebellum, and cranium. It also gives rise to the word *carrot*, which is derived from its horn shape. In Creek the word *keres* means horn. The Greek *kare* means head, from which our word cheer is derived. An obsolete definition of cheer is the face; for example, Shakespeare, in *A Midsummer Night's Dream*, wrote, "all fancy sike she is, and pale of cheere." It also came to mean the look or expression of the face, and from this to mean someone's state of mind as reflected in the face. And the smile we see on the face leads us to believe that the person is cheerful.

Gall Bladder Meridian

The meridian of adoration

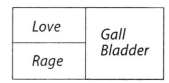

Love	Gall Bladder
Rage	

Negative Emotions:	Rage Fury Wrath
Positive Affirmations:	I reach out with love. I reach out with forgiveness.
Test Image:	Someone has just done something very infuriating. He has just read your most personal letters and your private diary without your permission. You are shouting at him. You want to hit him.

Rage and Fury

The gall bladder meridian's negative emotional state is that of *rage.* Rage comes from the Latin *rabere*, which means to be furiously angry. From the Latin, we get not only the word *rage* itself, but also such words as *rave* and the *rabid*, "mad dog."

Rage is defined as "violent anger, furious passion, usually manifested in looks, words or action." In Buck's survey of many European languages, he states that the words for *rage* and *fury* "are specialised from 'mental excitement,' based in part upon notions of violent physical action."

The test point for the gall bladder meridian. At or just below the junction of the ninth rib and the costal border.

ÆTATIS · SVE · 88 ·

Most people will test weak for the gall bladder meridian when looking at this photo. Saying the positive affirmation for the gall bladder meridian will overcome the weakness.

Another dictionary states, "Rage and fury are closely related in the sense of intense, uncontained, explosive emotion." The close relationship between rage and fury is perhaps best exemplified in Johnson's dictionary, where he calls rage "violent anger; vehement fury." It is the combination of the anger with the violence, the acting out of the anger. Shakespeare in *Coriolanus* referred to it as "this tiger footed rage."

The difference between rage and anger is that rage carries a sense of doing something about one's anger. Rage is in a sense the physical manifestation of anger. It is the act or the strong wish to act on the anger. Anger does not specify the manner of expression, but rage implies that something will be done.

Not surprisingly, the positive transmutation is not just the thinking of love, but the conceptualising of love in an active form. Instead of reaching out to strike the object of the rage, think of reaching out to love him or her. The affirmation we use here is, "I reach out with love."

The emotional continuum for the gall bladder meridian is not merely ranging from anger to love or forgiveness, as it is for the heart meridian (see page 72), but rather it is from violent, active anger to love and forgiveness, with the added concept of movement toward the other person with that particular emotion. We say in the positive, "I reach out with love. I come forward with love and forgiveness." When we turn to the positive, we find as in Ezekiel 21:17, "I will cause my fury to rest."

Wrath

Another negative emotional attribute of the gall bladder meridian is *wrath*, which has been defined as violent, resentful anger; rage; fury. Again, we can see that it is more than anger, it is the acting on the anger; the violence; the violent act associated with the anger. Wordsworth wrote, "On he drives with cheeks that burn/ In downright fury and in wrath." "In wrath remember mercy." (Habakkuk 3:2)

Choler

Choler was one of the four humors of medieval medicine, denoting bitter anger and wrath. It comes from the Latin *cholera*, which meant bile or wrath, as well as the disease. *Chol* (see *melan-choly* page 93) refers to the bile in the gall bladder, from which we get *cholecystectomy,* the removal of the gall bladder. Gower wrote in 1390 *(Confessio Amantis* III), "The drie coler with his hete, By wey of kinde his propre sete Hath in the galle, where he dwelleth," illustrating the relationship between gall and hate—which we have corroborated six hundred years later through our research.

Who else but Shakespeare, in *The Taming of the Shrew,* could so beautifully play on the relationship between anger and bile. In Act IV, Petruchio throws some meat which he has been served about the stage. Katharine says, "I pray you, husband, be not so disquiet: The meat was well, if you were so contented." Petruchio replies, "I tell thee, Kate, 'twas burnt and dried away; And I expressly am forbid to touch it, For it engenders choler, planteth anger; And better 'twere that both of us did fast, Since, of ourselves, ourselves are choleric, Than feed it with such over-roasted flesh." He is alluding to the belief that it was the excess bile that led to the humor of choler, wrath to excess.

I was once visiting the office of a friend of mine who is a doctor of osteopathy. A woman was brought in who during the previous night had suddenly developed a wrist drop due to a muscular paralysis. She lay down on his treatment table and he spent the next hour manipulating her hand and neck. Although he had made quite definite changes in the structural balance, the wrist drop persisted, unchanged. He then told me that he did not know what else to do to take the pressure off the involved nerve and relieve the paralysis. He asked me for a suggestion, but I had none, as I had never worked with such a case. I decided to check her meridians. I found that she had an energy imbalance in the gall bladder meridian. For the duration of her treatment she had been lying passively on the table, but when I asked her, "Are you really angry about something? Is there something or someone making you furious?" she immediately sat bolt upright and said, "Yes, there certainly is!" Then she launched into a tirade of anger and rage about the hospital in which her mother had died only a few days earlier. Every muscle of her body was contracted into a gesture of total rage—every muscle except the paralysed one in her right hand. The rage subsided and she lay down again. My friend then re-examined her neck and reported that there had been a great change—all the muscles were loose and free, and there was greater mobility in the neck and shoulder. He felt something had been unlocked. The muscle was still paralysed, but he was confident enough to advise her to go home and rest and call the next day.

I was alarmed. My medical training said that this was a severe condition. I thought, "She needs cervical X rays. She needs myelograms. She may need a spinal tap. This could be a serious condition. She needs hospitalisation!" But she called the next morning to report that she was cured. That was a year ago, and there has been no recurrence.

This was not a hysterical episode. She had a definite paralysis in the muscles of her hand, as confirmed by neurological testing. What had happened, I presume, was that the rage she was feeling toward the hospital had caused a distinct pattern of severe contraction of certain muscles which had then pulled the bony structures of the neck and shoulder. This had caused an interference with the nerve supply from the neck to the muscles of the wrist. She needed the osteopathic treatment to release the musculature, as my friend had attempted. But she also required correction of the rage which, after all, was the primary problem in this case. When both the physical and psychological procedures were carried out, her symptoms were relieved and she was spared what could have been prolonged and traumatic medical and neurological investigation. The osteopath acknowledged the importance of the psychological work. Yet all I had done was cheek the meridians, a simple procedure, and ask her one question. It took less than a minute. Certainly it would not have succeeded without the osteopathic intervention, but just as certainly, the osteopathic treatment was greatly enhanced by this simple, yet valuable, procedure.

Adoration

The best word for the process of overcoming rage is *adoration.* It is defined as "the act of worshipping, or paying divine honours," and "the exhibition of profound regard and love." It is from the Latin *ad*—to—and *orare*—to pray. This adoration overcomes rage. Rage is anger in action; adoration is love in action, a reaching out with love.

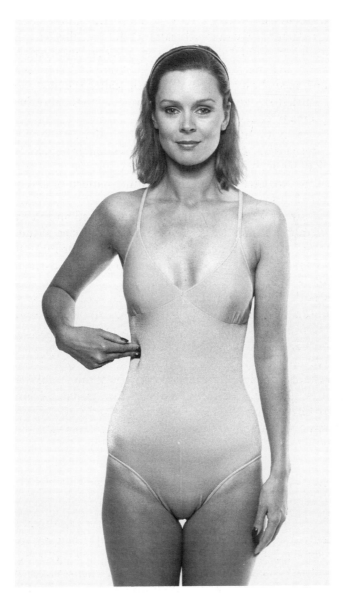

The test point for the spleen meridian. Tip of the eleventh rib.

Spleen Meridian

The meridian of confidence

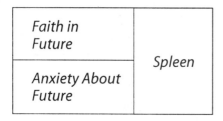

Faith in Future	Spleen
Anxiety About Future	

Negative Emotion: Realistic anxieties about the future

Positive Affirmations: I have faith and confidence in my future. I am secure. My future is secure.

Test Image: Next month's bills are before you. You do not have the money to pay them, and you can see no way of coming up with it.

Realistic Anxieties About the Future

The spleen meridian supplies energy to both the spleen and the pancreas, and we find that it is frequently involved in patients who have hypoglycemia (low blood sugar). This condition is a very common problem today. The test point for this meridian is the tip of the eleventh rib on each side.

The specific state involved in spleen meridian problems is one of worry and anxiety about the future, about real problems in the relatively immediate future. "Where is next month's rent coming from?" "Will I be able to go back to college next year?" "How can I pay my wife's medical bills?" "Am I going to be fired from my job? If I am fired, what other work can I do?" These very real practical problems seem to affect the spleen meridian.[16]

The positive affirmation here is, "I have faith and confidence in my future." I recognise that I have a path in life, and to the best of my abilities, I am trying to determine my true goals, and I am trying to act accordingly. I recognise that if I try to do what is right, I have no need to feel anxiety and worry about the future. Or, if my motives are clean and good, good will come to me. I have

Most people will test weak for the spleen meridian when looking at this photograph. The positive affirmation for the spleen meridian will overcome the weakness.

faith. I have confidence. I can advance forward, knowing that what is right for me will come to me.

The state of faith and confidence brought about by these affirmations overcomes spleen-meridian problems. This affirmation is used a great deal, because so many people have a spleen-meridian energy problem. We live in an age of anxiety about the future. Furthermore, the refined foods we eat predispose us to blood sugar disturbance, which also affects the energy in the spleen meridian.

In Johnson's dictionary we find that confidence means "assured beyond doubt." We also find confidence meaning "secure of success; without fear of miscarriage."

Secure

Someone who is "confident in expectation" is secure. To be secure means to be "free from fear or doubt; not anxious or unsure," and "not likely to fail." The word derives from the Latin *se*, without, and *cura*, care, attention (hence *cure*). The literal meaning is thus without care or anxiety, but the virtual meaning is "without cause for anxiety, safe." And *security* is "freedom from care, anxiety or apprehension."

Imagine that you are swinging on a trapeze bar high above the ground. You are about to let go and sail through the air, your arms outstretched to grab the other bar coming toward you. How fearful you would be in this situation depends on whether there is a safety net. If a safety net is there, it does not matter if you fall. You will not be hurt, and all you have to do is climb up the ladder and try again. But if there is no safety net, you may die.

Every day of our lives we are being invited to release one bar and fly to another one. Every day we are being given a chance to let go of what we have and, with faith and confidence in our future, to reach out for a better way, a better life. Often, rather than welcoming the situation, we are fearful. We hold back because we do not believe there is a safety net. We believe that if we miss we will die, and thus it is better to hold back, even better not to develop, than to run the risk of dying. But if you feel that the new bar will come, and you have the deep and secure knowledge that there is a safety net, then you will take the risk.

I have observed many small babies being swept up into the air and even momentarily let go and then caught again in their mother's arms. Some will laugh with glee and others will exhibit a startled reaction of fear. Already some of them know that they have a safety net they can trust—the foundation of which is the mother's love. If we are secure in our mother's love we are free to fly anywhere. We are free to take giant leaps, free to explore, free to let go and await the right way. We are secure. This safety net not only provides the freedom to explore in the world, it also gives a freedom to explore inside ourselves. It gives us the courage to have insight, to look at ourselves as we truly are.[17]

When faced with realistic concerns about the future, it is helpful to affirm "I am secure. My future is secure." With this secure confidence, your spleen meridian energy will be positive and you will be in a better position to make constructive decisions and find a creative solution.

It is not uncommon to find the safety net syndrome in people who have blood sugar disturbances. Often they seem overburdened with realistic anxieties about the future. Many of my hypoglycemic or diabetic patients push themselves beyond their limits in an attempt to obtain material security. This pattern usually long predates their physical symptoms. They fear that if something goes wrong, there will be no one there to catch them, no support. They have no trust in the future. They struggle hard to build security through possessions, money, position, and so forth, in order to protect themselves from the feared fall. It is as if Mother has not provided them with a safety net, so they are going to make their own.

Consider Brenda, a twenty-three-year-old woman who suddenly developed diabetes last month. I discussed the safety net syndrome with her and she saw many similarities with her life. Ever since she was very young she had feared for the future. She worried that something would go wrong, that she would never have enough money, food, or clothes. As soon as she was old enough, she found part-time jobs to make sure she had enough for "a rainy day."

Yet only a few years earlier she had made a very brave decision. She left her native Greece and moved to America, even though she had only one relative in the country. She initially stayed with him and his family in Syracuse. He looked after her and protected her as she adjusted to the new country. His family became her safety net. Then she decided to move to New York City with her new boyfriend. They found a small apartment and settled down, but soon she became very apprehensive. He could not find steady employment, and she had no special skills. She managed to find a job, but the salary was very low. There was a constant nagging fear in her mind that she wouldn't be able to make the rent. She saved as much as possible from each week's pay to make sure there would be enough when the rent was due. The financial burden became hers completely, as her boyfriend still had not found a steady job. She became preoccupied with the thought, "What if something goes wrong and I'm fired, or get sick. Then there won't be enough money to pay the rent. We will be put out in the street." Her anxieties were compounded by the fact that she had not yet obtained her immigration papers, and she was worried that she could be deported. The crowning worry was the fear that her boyfriend would fall out of love with her and kick her out of the apartment, leaving her stranded, completely alone, and virtually broke. Then one evening a woman called and asked to speak to him. Brenda suspected this was one of his old girlfriends. Suddenly her safety net, thin as it was, disappeared altogether. A month later she developed diabetes.

Of course, many other people survive similar circumstances without developing diabetes. But in Brenda's case, due to her particular makeup, physically and psychologically, this was the result. Her medical treatments will be supplemented with the specific affirmations for the spleen meridian, "I have faith and confidence in my future. I am secure. My future is secure."

Kidney Meridian

The meridian of sexual assuredness

Sexual Security	Kidney
Sexual Indecision	

Negative Emotion:	Sexual Indecision
Positive Affirmations:	I am sexually secure.
	My sexual energies are balanced.
Test Image:	You are having sex with an acquaintance— someone you are not particularly attracted to, yet are not totally turned off by.

The test point for the kidney meridian. Tip of the twelfth rib.

Most people will test weak for the kidney meridian when looking at this photo. Saying the positive affirmation for the kidney meridian will overcome the weakness.

Sexual Indecision

The kidney meridian's negative emotional states are related to *sexual indecision*. The test point for this meridian is the tip of the twelfth rib. We frequently find kidney meridian problems in people who cannot make up their minds about a sexual problem. "Should I sleep with this man?" "Do I really want to?" "Am I ready for this sort of involvement?" These types of problems tend to affect the kidney meridian.

The problems here can be very subtle. For example, I have frequently found weaknesses on testing men who are having problems with their wives, and are even possibly contemplating having affairs. It will show up with anyone who is experiencing not so much sexual dissatisfaction as sexual indecision.

The transmutation of sexual indecision is the positive affirmation, "My sexual energies are balanced." I encourage my patients with this problem to state this affirmation as part of their daily program. I tell them, "There is some sort of sexual indecision troubling you. What I suggest is that you try to make a decision, even if you make the positive decision not to make a decision until some point in the future. Stop letting the problem drain your kidney meridian energy. Make a decision about what is bothering you, and then file it away. Don't let it take up all your time, attention, and energy." Usually patients are eager to correct the problem, and follow my advice. I do not know what they are thinking or doing privately, but when they come back, they usually test strong. We have had fine changes in people's personalities and often in their kidney problems when they have made this sexual decision. The patient is further strengthened when he reaffirms his decision with the affirmation, "My sexual energies are balanced."

I remember a man who, on the several occasions when I tested him, had a kidney meridian problem. He was a very strait-laced, proper, religious man who, I thought, was happily married and devoted to his wife. One day I said to him, "You are contemplating having an affair with another woman." He looked at me in amazement and said, "How did you know?" I said, "That's what your body is telling me—that is what a continuous weakness in the kidney-meridian energy supply often indicates." He then told me that he was undecided about having an affair with his secretary. He recognised that he loved his wife but was also infatuated with his secretary; he didn't know what he should do. Hence, the sexual indecision.

I told him, "I'm not your judge. I am not telling you whether you should have an affair or not. But what I am suggesting to you is that your continuing indecision about the affair is interfering with your kidney meridian energy."

When he returned next, I found that his kidney meridian tested strong. I asked if he had made his decision. He said that he had, and that he was going to have the affair with his secretary. Of course I am not advocating this as the solution to kidney meridian problems. It seems to me that he could just as easily have made the decision not to have the sexual encounter with his secretary. The important point here is that ongoing sexual indecision seems to lead to kidney meridian imbalances.

I remember a woman who had had several episodes of renal colic. She also, not surprisingly, had a recurrent kidney-meridian energy weakness. When I questioned her about her sexual indecision, she confided that for quite some time she had been debating whether to encourage one of the tradesmen coming to her house, as she was becoming more and more dissatisfied with her sex life with her husband. Incidentally, she also suffered from bruxism—night grinding (think on that expression for a minute). Both the night grinding and her kidney disturbance disappeared after she made the sexual decision. She decided to give up the thoughts of the other man and instead to concentrate on rekindling her sexual relationship with her husband.

In every case of kidney disease there may not be a state of sexual indecision. But in my practice I have found this to be the case so often that it would surprise me if I did find a case of renal impairment where there was not sexual indecision at some level.

The most characteristic feature of Beethoven's music is its underlying expression of a kidney meridian problem. Not coincidentally, he had a large kidney stone.[18]

Many illustrated advertisements, particularly those for cosmetics and toiletries and certain types of clothing, tend to interfere with the energy flow in the kidney meridian. This effect may well not be accidental.

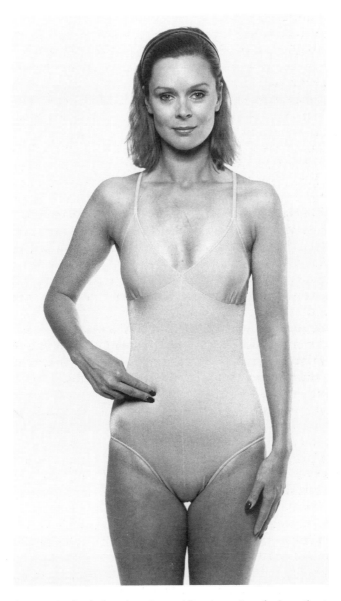

The test point for the large intestine meridian. Approximately six centimetres lateral to the umbilicus and two centimetres below.

Large Intestine Meridian

The meridian of self-worth

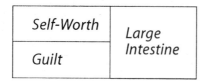

Self-Worth	Large Intestine
Guilt	

Negative Emotion: Guilt
Positive Affirmations: I am basically clean and good.
                        I am worthy of being loved.

Test Image: You have just done something over which
                       you feel extremely guilty. Use an example
                       from your own life.

Guilt

Melanie Klein found that the origins of guilt lay in what she called the depressive position,[19] the second stage of the psychic development of the child, the depression and consequent guilt being in response to the child's anger, hatred, and envy of the mother. Thus we frequently find that there will be a close relationship between the thyroid meridian, which has to do with depression, and the large intestine meridian. In clinical practice, we frequently hear people who feel depressed say that they feel guilty. In fact, many will say they feel so guilty over what they have done that they should not have their depression treated, that they don't deserve to be treated. Also, very frequently, severe depressives will be constipated. In fact, they will often remark how their bowels are full of evil and badness.

I have seen many patients with ulcerative colitis, a disease of the bowel. Every one of them has had a deep sense of guilt, a punishing conscience. I have had some fortunate successes with these patients, one of the major reasons for which is that I have always, very early in treatment, shown these people how their bodies are saying that they feel guilty. Then we try to discuss their guilt and I ask them to say the positive affirmation, "I am basically clean and good. I am worthy of being loved." Very frequently these

Most people will test weak for the large intestine meridian when looking at this photo. Saying the positive affirmation for the large intestine meridian will overcome the weakness.

people say, "Yes, you're right, my conscience is killing me." Often, an ulcerative colitis patient will call me up and say, "Doctor, my bowel is acting up again. There's something I'm feeling really guilty about." When they say the affirmation it almost invariably leads to a reduction of their colitis symptoms.

At the beginning of this book I stated that in my early days of practice I began to feel that professionally I wasn't good enough. I felt that if I knew more, if I were more conscientious, if I spent longer hours with the patients, if I had taken better histories, if I had attended more conferences to learn more about the various diseases, if I had spent more time talking to the relatives—then perhaps the patients would have improved more. This professional guilt haunted me.

I first became aware of the relationship between guilt and large intestine disease when I was a young resident. A boy of eighteen was admitted to the hospital to have nearly all his large bowel removed for ulcerative colitis. I talked to him at great length because it worried me and puzzled me that he was having this surgery. In fact, I felt terrified and somewhat ashamed that this was all the treatment our profession had to offer—removal of nearly all the large intestine of a young man. The one outstanding characteristic that came through to me in my naive psychological understanding at that time was how very responsible this boy was for his family. His father had died when he was thirteen, and the boy had assumed the entire responsibility for both his family and the farm that they owned. He supervised the education of the other children, insisted on doing all the shopping for his mother, managed the family's finances, and it seemed he put in very nearly a full day's farming, seven days a week, as well as attending school until he became old enough to leave legally. He was already, when I first saw him, in many ways an old family man, weighed down by responsibilities. What I now know, which I did not know then, is that almost invariably when someone takes on such a load as this, it is out of a sense of guilt.

The price he paid for this was great. Soon he was back in the hospital again and this time the colitis had spread from his large intestine up to his small intestine; not long afterward he died, a victim of his overburdening guilt.

Guilt can be an incredibly powerful negative emotion. Conversely, it is rare to find people who, without false pride or conceit, have a sense of their own self-worth and a legitimate and real pride in themselves and their lives. So many of us, it seems, are ridden with guilt—and so many of us have bowel problems.

The next time you have constipation or mild diarrhoea, test your large intestine meridian energy. If it tests weak, say the appropriate affirmations repeatedly and see if they assist you. This technique has helped many people.

We see that the negative large intestine meridian emotion of guilt is really a form of self-hatred and low self-esteem. The guilt-ridden person is always blaming himself or herself for what goes wrong in his or her own life and often in the lives of family and friends. According to Johnson, guilt originally signified the fine paid for an offence, and later it came to mean the offence itself. It is not only the offence but also the mental attitude that accompanies the offence, I would say.

Guilt is derived from the Anglo-Saxon word *gylt*, which meant a crime. Guilt is now defined as "the state (meriting condemnation and reproach of conscience) of having wilfully committed a crime or heinous moral offence; criminality, great culpability." It has often been said that "a guilty conscience needs no accuser." When we feel guilty, then, we feel like criminals. We feel we should be punished because we are no good.

Thus, the "seat" of our conscience is in the large intestine. This is where all our primitive guilt attacks us. Whenever you hear of someone with bowel problems, whenever you find someone who continually tests weak at the large intestine point—not just occasionally, but continually—you know that this person has a deep sense of guilt, a strong punishing conscience. This is someone who does not love himself.

Psychologically, people who feel guilty tend to be obsessional; they tend to feel they are not clean enough. This heavy burden of guilt (dirt) is why they are, for example, always washing their hands. As you might expect, I always find that they have large intestine meridian energy imbalances. Those who are unfortunate enough to become psychotic or schizophrenic often, when they are severely ill, will scream that they are all dirty inside, they are full of faeces, they are full of dirt.

The positive affirmation that counteracts the effects of guilt is, "I am worthy of being loved" and/or "I am basically clean and good."[20]

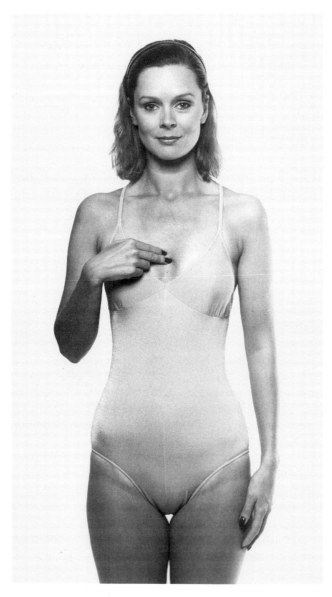

The test point for the circulation sex meridian. Approximately level with nipples.

"Midline" Meridians

Those meridians whose test points are in the midline:
Circulation-Sex
Heart
Stomach
Thyroid
Small Intestine
Bladder

One of these meridians will test weak when the subject is left-hemisphere dominant.

Circulation-Sex Meridian

The meridian of relaxation, generosity, and abjuration

Circulation Sex	Renunciation of Past, Generosity, Relaxation
	Jealousy, Sexual Tension, Regret, Remorse

Negative Emotions:	Regret and Remorse Sexual Tension Jealousy Stubbornness
Positive Affirmations:	I renounce the past. I am relaxed. My body is relaxed. I am generous.
Test Image:	You are in the midst of a long project, and it seems that the project will never be completed. You sincerely regret that you ever began it.

> You are thinking of a person who really turns you on, and the more you think about this person, the more excited you become.

> You find your lover with a rival and you are trying to figure a way of getting your lover away from the rival and back for yourself.

The circulation-sex meridian is a very complicated meridian as it supplies energy to two major organs of the body, most of whose functions are quite separate. These are the adrenal glands, which almost as much as the thymus gland determine our responses to physiological stress, and the sexual glands (the ovaries and testes) and the associated sexual organs. The positive and negative emotional states associated with this meridian are of three basic types. Because these types do not seem to bear a great deal of relationship among themselves, I am inclined to think that this may be a complex meridian that has not yet been completely mapped out. There may be some subdivisions of this meridian still to be enumerated. Perhaps the adrenals and the sex glands are subserved by the same meridian because they both secrete sex hormones. Or perhaps at some deep level, somewhere in the realms of the unconscious, the two apparently separate emotions of jealousy and regret are related.

Regret

The first negative emotion of the circulation-sex meridian which we will consider is *regret*. This word is derived from the Old Norse word *grata*, which meant to weep, and in Northern English the word still has this meaning. There is a Scottish song that says, "Around my feet are twenty-one greeting wains." (Wains are children).

Regret has been defined as: "Sorrow or disappointment due to some external circumstance or event"; and "sorrow or pain due to reflection on something one has done or left undone."[21]

Cowper wrote of the "scenes that I love, and with regret perceive Forsaken, or through folly not enjoyed."[22] Shelley wrote that "pining regrets, and vain repentances ... pervade Their valueless

Most people will test weak for the circulation-sex meridian when looking at this photo. Saying the positive affirmation for the circulation-sex meridian will overcome the weakness.

and miserable lives ."[23] Johnson defines regret as "vexation at something past."

As you can see, the basic meaning of the word *regret* seems to be a feeling of particular displeasure on looking back. The English word *grede*, which has the same origin as regret, means to cry or to wail.

Remorse

Remorse has been defined as bitter regret. It comes from the Latin *mordere*, to bite. The idea it gives is to bite again, or to bite afterward; that is, after the traumatic event has passed it is still biting at us, it is still attacking us. The past is still hurting us. We have not let it go.

Nearly every person I test who has been through a divorce will test as having a sense of regret and remorse. There is a holding on to the past, an unwillingness to let it go, to say, "That was my past life. It is no longer me. I am going my way. She is going her way. Our paths are now separate," and to have no hang-ups or ties to this past life. There is a reluctance or an inability to acknowledge the good parts, to forgive the bad, and to move forward into the present, renouncing the past, living life day by day. This ability to release the past is rarely found in people who have been divorced.

Regret and remorse thus both imply a holding on to the past. When I work with people who have a recurrent circulation-sex-meridian energy imbalance I often find it necessary to spend considerable time showing them how it is affecting them and encouraging them to release the past. Tears are often required to accomplish this release or renunciation. The easiest "technique" is to encourage the person to co-ordinate his breath with saying, "I renounce the past." He or she takes in a big breath and then slowly lets it all out while thinking that as he or she is letting the air out, the past is being released, being let go.

A circulation-sex meridian imbalance is often found in people who experienced a broken love affair from which they have never recovered. I recall a man who came to see me complaining that he had no energy. He was always tired, always run down, he had one cold or sore throat after another, he never seemed to be well, and he had great difficulty in making any form of close contact with women. He recognised that he did want to have acloserelationship, but somehow he could not manage to develop it. On testing we found a recurrent circulation-sex-meridian energy imbalance.

I then learned from him that he had once had an affair with one of the women at his office. He was deeply in love with her, and they spent several wonderful months together. However, she started hinting to him that perhaps everything wasn't right between them, and gradually she told him that she felt they should break up their relationship. She did not leave him for someone else, but merely because she found it increasingly difficult to get along with him. He was shattered. For months and months afterward he analysed their times together and wondered what he had done to "ruin" the relationship. He began to dwell on the past, not just reminiscing over their good times together but also looking for clues as to why they had broken up. They still worked in the same office, and he found it more and more difficult to walk past her desk without feeling very upset.

After discussing this problem with him, I suggested that he recognise that he must release the past and get on with his present life. He did work on this, and he often said the positive affirmation, "I renounce the past," to himself. He realised that his attitude toward this past affair was hampering any possible relationships he might form in the present. Eventually he was able to walk past his ex-girlfriend's desk without becoming upset, and he even found it possible to carry on social conversations with her—something he had been unable to do since she suggested that they end their affair.

Within a short period of time his life energy increased, he felt better in general, and he was able to relate to women in a much more satisfactory manner. The continual energy drain associated with his circulation-sex-meridian energy imbalance had been corrected and he was now able to use his energies more creatively and effectively.

We also find this meridian imbalance frequently in adults who complain about the way in which their parents brought them up. They will say, "I regret the fact that my parents didn't treat me better. If they had given me a different type of education, or if they hadn't been so strict, or if they hadn't been so lenient-or whatever." These people are caught in the past and blaming it for their troubles in the present. They must be encouraged to say, "That is done. It is past. I will let it go and move on in the present."

Others who often develop energy imbalances in the circulation-sex meridian are people who have been involved in serious tragedies-accidents and so forth. At some level they will generally test as undergoing bouts of remorse and regret. When they recognise that such thoughts are a source of continual energy drain and when they begin to use the positive affirmations, they gradually renounce the past and accept it, deciding to move forward. In such a manner we may even achieve the Zen state of "my mind is wholly disconnected with things of the past."

Renunciation of the Past

I have been unable to find one word to describe the precise positive emotion that is the antonym of regret and remorse. Through clinical testing, we have found that the affirmation that corrects these two emotional states is, *"I renounce the past."* What is necessary to correct these negative emotional states, then, is a letting go of the past. That way all our life energy may be concentrated upon the present and achieving our true goal.

It may even be tenable to suggest that a definition of psychiatric normality would be the ability not to bring the past to bear on a present problem, for example, the ability not to be upset by what a friend does today when it reminds you of a similar occurrence with another friend in the past which was unpleasant for you. In love affairs, we must remember not to carry over problems from previous affairs into the present.

Imagine that you are looking for a hard-to-find item. You may go from store to store trying to obtain it. After trying several, you get angry with the sales clerk at the next store—not because he did not have the item so much as because you had been unable to find it so many other times previously. You have carried over the resentments from the previous stores. Of course, you should approach this store as if it were the first. And in a situation involving an intimate relationship, we should deal with each person as if he or she were the first.

Thus it is throughout life. Often we attempt to deal with a problem that exists in the present in a manner that is clouded with those of the past. Instead, we should be able to treat it afresh, not bringing with us the "baggage" from the past. In one sense, this is what a psychiatrist attempts to do with his patients-getting them to deal with the present in the present, not with predetermined ideas as to how the problem will be solved because of patterns that eventuated in the past. We must renounce the past and deal with the present as just that. In Genesis 19:17 we read, "Look not behind thee." In Luke 9:62, "No man, having put his hand to the plow, and looking back, is fit for the kingdom of God."

The word I most prefer for the process of overcoming regret is *abjuration*, which is defined as a "solemn or formal renunciation or giving up of anything." It is often used in a legal sense, even as an oath, reinforcing the renunciation process by making it more definite, deliberate and binding. *Jury*, a body of people who swear to hear and give a verdict, is from the same root. Regret involves holding on to the past; abjuration is an undertaking to let it go, a foreswearing.

Tension

Another negative emotional attitude of the circulation-sex meridian is that of sexual *tension*. This is a very common finding. You will discover on testing that many advertisements affect this meridian. Present-day clothing often affects this meridian, as do many of the titillating advertisements in newspapers, magazines, and on hoardings. (Remember the pretty girl in the car ads, for example.) Many of these ads are designed, unconsciously if you will, to make us feel sexually tense. In this state of tension we will act to resolve the aroused meridian imbalance—and this action is often to the benefit of the advertiser or the promoter. One marketing expert told me that in the example of the automobile ads the "pretty girl" was used as the come-on to entice the man to buy, only he was subconsciously not buying the car at all, but the "mistress" who accompanied it in the ads. He said further that in more recent ads for cars a handsome man is often used, because there are more single women out on their own now who are buying cars for themselves and more married women who are now getting their own cars. I would suspect that such advertising expertise is not limited to the marketing of automobiles.

The penalty we pay for the "excitement" introduced by such advertising is a weakening of the energy flow in the circulation-sex meridian. This in turn affects our adrenal glands.

Note here that I am not saying that all tension is of a sexual nature, although it is much more common than we may realise. Remember that whenever there is stress, at some level there will almost invariably be mental and/or physical tension—and there will also be stress effects on the adrenal glands.

We live in a state of stress and therefore one of tension. Added to this is the specific sexual tension that is so prevalent in our present society—the idea that we must constantly be seducing members of the opposite sex. No wonder this very complex meridian often tests as having energy imbalances.

Stubbornness

The emotional quality of *stubbornness* connotes the idea of rigidity, inflexibility, refusing to bend, mold, and adjust. Consider the business executive who has been successful by following one pattern of operation and who, when offered a more efficient method, refuses even to consider it. This rigidity or inflexibility comes from and then adds to tension.

Relaxation

The positive state that is opposite tension is *relaxation*. The word *relaxation* comes from the Latin *laxare*, which means to loosen, slacken, or soften. The word literally means to be lax or soft again. The *Oxford English Dictionary* in part defines relaxation as, "To render [a part of the body] less firm or rigid; to make loose or slack."

Since tension is a state of rigidity, the positive affirmation is a return once again to a lax, softer state. The sexual connotations here are obvious, and it is certainly not by coincidence that these emotional states are related to the meridian that supplies energy to the sex glands. The positive affirmations, "I am relaxed," or "My body is relaxed" have been found to restore the energy balance to the circulation-sex meridian.

Jealousy

Jealousy is derived from the Latin *zelus*, meaning zeal or fervour. The idea behind jealousy is that we act and even fight with zeal to protect and regain what we feel is rightfully ours. The *Oxford English Dictionary* says jealousy is "vigilance in guarding a possession." It involves a state of rivalry. It has been stated, perhaps metaphorically, that rivals may be considered as opponents on opposite river banks facing each other.[24] Thus, jealousy implies that we regard the possession (and a spouse or lover is regarded a possession in this context) as "ours" and one for which we will fight, if necessary, to regain.

Jealousy is always a triangular situation. The husband is jealous of the rival who has "made off " with his wife. So, with all his energy, he fights the rival to regain his wife for himself. Involved in this action is no concept of the wife as a separate person, making her own decision as to what she wants to do with her life and with whom she wants to spend it. In a jealousy situation there is always the feeling that the party fought for, the wife in this case, is seen purely as a possession, something to be regained. Love for the wife is of less importance than the wish on the part of the man to regain what is his. Owen Meredith wrote, "No true love there can be without its dread penalty—jealousy."[25] But jealousy is not love. It arises out of selfishness and a sense of possession of the other person, not out of a true loving relationship with him or her. Robert Louis Stevenson wrote, "jealousy, at any rate, is one of the consequences of love; you may like it or not, at pleasure; but there it is." I disagree. With true love there is no jealousy. We respect the wishes of the other person and out of love we want what is best for him or her as well as what is best for ourselves. La Rochefoucauld put it very well when he stated, "There is more self-love than love in jealousy."

The little child who refuses to share his toy with his siblings or playmates, defensively shouting, "It's mine, it's mine!" and clutching it with all his might is expressing jealousy, the unwillingness to share, the holding on to the possession at all costs.

Generosity

The positive emotion in this instance is generosity and sharing. Generosity is "the willingness to give or share." Johnson defines generosity as, "magnanimous; open of heart." It is a particularly appropriate word because the I-E root from which it is descended, *gen*[26] bears such words with a sexual connotation as *generation* and *gender*.

It is not surprising that jealousy is so prevalent today. In our society we have become so attached to our possessions that we guard them jealously. This may be related to an unwillingness to release the past. By contrast, *kindness*, which comes from the same root as generous (*gen*), means "of a friendly nature; generous or hospitable; warmhearted; good." Kindness is another positive attribute of the circulation-sex meridian.

We recently witnessed an example of jealousy among our cats. We obtained two female kittens from the same litter when they were ten weeks old. They are now over six months old and still play together, sleep together, and groom each other. When one is petted, held, or fed, the other doesn't seem to be upset by this but instead waits her turn. One is not jealous of the attention given to the other. Of course this in part stems' from their very early mothering. When we first brought home the new kittens, the cat that had been living with us for some years displayed all the signs which, if he were human, we would interpret as jealousy. He hissed at them and tried to drive them away from his "territory." It was as if he were trying to say to them, "This household is mine. I am going to protect it with all my energy. Go away. This is mine." If he were human we could have encouraged him to share and feel generous by counselling him. Because he is an animal, we simply displayed even more love toward him, spent more time with him, and tried for a gradual and gentle introduction to the kittens. However, he indignantly refused our offers of love and now refuses even to come into the house.

In some cases it is very difficult to overcome feelings of jealousy and stubbornness. With a patient or student, we would be able to counsel and assist him to overcome these negative emotional states through the appropriate affirmations and other work. Furthermore, we would work directly with his overall life energy as governed by his thymus gland, and activate it so that with love he could release his feelings of jealousy.

I once had a patient, a married man, who was having an affair with his secretary. I asked him if he felt that this affair was interfering with his relationship with his wife. He protested loudly, "Not at all, in fact, quite the contrary. My girlfriend has so stimulated my feelings of love that my wife is really the beneficiary of this increased love which is now being kindled." Some years later this same man came to me in tears. He had found out that his wife was having an affair and he felt he wanted to kill the man for what he had done to break up his household. He told me that he would fight for his wife with all his might because he simply was not going to lose her.

This story tempts me to repeat La Rochefoucauld's statement

The test point for the heart meridian. Tip of xiphoid process below sternum.

that jealousy is more self-love than love. After carefully discussing this man's history with him and explaining to him the negative effects on his own energy that this unbridled jealousy was creating, I was able to suggest that he use the affirmations "I am generous" and "My body is relaxed." He recognised that jealousy and sexual tension were draining his energy and preventing him from arriving at an unstressed solution to the problem at hand. It was not long before he had resolved his problem satisfactorily.

Heart Meridian

The meridian of forgiveness

Heart	*Love Forgiveness*
	Anger

Negative Emotion:	Anger
Positive Affirmations:	I love.
	I forgive.
	There is forgiveness in my heart.
Test Image:	You come back from a walk in the neighbourhood and catch a vandal in the act of letting the air out of the tyres of your car.

Anger

As previously discussed, the predominant negative emotion relating to the heart meridian is *anger.* This emotional state, and problems with this meridian, are very prominent in patients who have heart ailments.

Examining the origin of the word *anger*, we can see relationships between the heart and anger which we otherwise would not have suspected. The I-E root from which anger is derived is *angk,* which meant to choke or oppress. This of course is the exact feeling that people have when they suffer from the cardiac condi-

Most people will test weak for the heart meridian when looking at this photo. Saying the positive affirmation for the heart meridian will overcome the weakness.

tion of *angina pectoris.* The word *angina* is derived from this same root. In Latin, the word is *angere,* which means to strangle.

In Middle English, *anger* was more passive than it is now. It meant trouble and affliction, no longer having the more violent connotation of strangling and torture. Now, the word has yet another meaning. It means in a sense a retribution and the feeling provoked against a person who has troubled, afflicted, or tortured us. Perhaps anger was best described by John Locke, "Anger is uneasiness or discomfiture of the mind, upon the receipt of an injury, with a present purpose of revenge."

It is evident from Locke's definition that anger has revenge as its purpose. To stop the negative effects of the anger there must be a counteracting quality of forgiveness. To forgive is to pardon.

South wrote, "Anger is, according to some, a transient hatred, or at least very like it." As we know from our testing, hatred is a basic negative thymus attribute, while anger is associated with the heart meridian.

Forgiveness

Forgive means "to give up resentment or claim to requital for pardon (an offence)." Robert Burns wrote, "Fain would I say, 'Forgive my foul offence!'" It has been said that forgiveness is the renunciation of anger or resentment. It is this renouncing, this giving up of anger and resentment that turns the weakening effect on the heart meridian energy—and therefore on the heart—into a positive energy state. This is a good example of transmutation. We **are** transmuting anger into love and forgiveness, turning weakening effects into strengthening ones.

Most primitive words for forgiveness involve giving or letting go. We can think of forgiveness as releasing anger and giving love. As the Bible says, "For if ye forgive men their trespasses, your heavenly Father will also forgive you." (Matthew 6:14) Johnson described forgiveness as "tenderness; willingness to pardon." And Dryden wrote:

> Mercy above did hourly plead
> For her resemblance here below;
> And mild forgiveness intercede
> To stop the coming blow.

Anger, of course, is a very common finding. Its cure is forgiveness. Yet often today we seem to have the idea that the cure of anger is what we would call a psychological enema—to get it all out, really tell the object of your anger off, get it out of your system. On testing you will find that this does not cure the anger. Instead you will discover that not only does the angry person still have the heart-meridian energy imbalance, but the person who has been the object of the angry outburst will now also have this meridian imbalance. He or she now has resentment, "feels back," toward you.[27] Thus the "cure" of anger is not to let it all out but instead to transmute it into love, into forgiveness. This can be done instantly when the life energy, the will to be well, is activated.

The next time you are driving and encounter a traffic jam, have someone in the car test you. You will find that being in such a situation usually produces a heart meridian imbalance. "He that is slow to anger is better than the mighty." (Proverbs 16:32)

Stomach Meridian

The meridian of contentment and tranquility

Stomach	Contentment
	Disappointment Disgust, Greed

Negative Emotions:
    Disgust
    Disappointment
    Bitterness
    Greed
    Emptiness
    Deprivation
    Nausea
    Hunger

Positive Affirmations:
    I am content.
    I am tranquil.

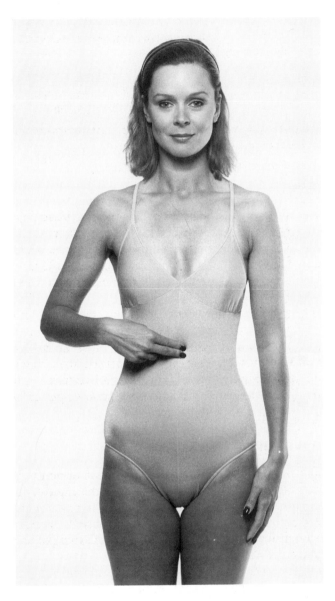

The test point for the stomach meridian. Halfway between xiphoid process and umbilicus.

Test Image: You are walking down the street and see your lover strolling arm-in-arm with someone else. You realise that you have been displaced.

You have been in line for a promotion for some time. When the vacancy occurs, someone else is given the job.

The emotional states associated with the stomach meridian quite obviously relate to stomach functions.

Disgust

Disgust is "strong distaste or disrelish for food; sickening physical disinclination to partake of food, drink, medicine, etc., nausea, loathing." It is also defined as "strong repugnance, aversion or repulsion excited by that which is loathesome or offensive," as a foul smell, disagreeable person or action, disappointed ambition, and so on.

Disgust initially comes from the Latin *gustare*, to taste. The word really means something that tastes bad, that causes us to sicken, even to vomit to expel it. The word *choose* comes from the same root as disgust. Thus we can say that we choose either to keep or to spit out things that are of good taste or bad taste—things we do or do not relish. Johnson defines the verb *to disgust* as "to raise aversion in the stomach; to distaste."

Disappointment

Disappointment is defined as "the frustration or nonfulfillment of expectation, intention, or desire," and as "the anguish of disappointed faith." The word comes from the Latin *puntare*, meaning to fix the points. *Punctum* in Latin means point of agreement. In Middle English disappointment took on the meaning of removing from office and dispossessing.

Today the basic meaning is removal from our appointment, from our relationship with another person. The boyfriend takes a new girl friend, and the first girl friend experiences disappointment. The points of agreement have been broken, and she has been removed from office, so to speak—dispossessed of her particular relationship with her man.

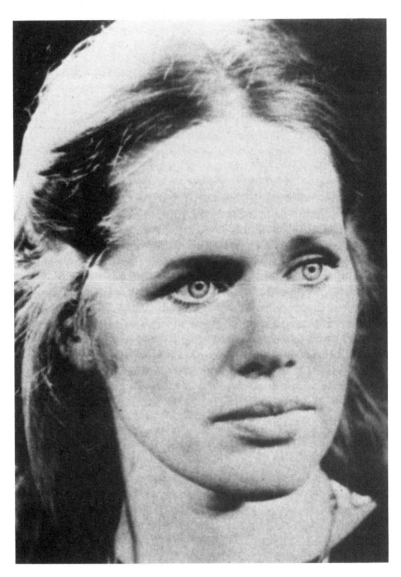

Most people will test weak for the stomach meridian when looking at this photo. Saying the positive affirmation for the stomach meridian will overcome the weakness.

Consider what I meant when I stated that I felt disappointed in my practice. From everything I had been taught I had been led to believe that if I did certain things my patients would be better, and happy, and would go about their lives full and complete and realised. This is what I expected, but it did not materialise. This led to my feelings of disappointment. My disappointment came about because what I had been led to believe would arrive in point of fact did not arrive, in the same way the baby is led to believe that if he is hungry Mummy will provide food. If the food does not arrive, he feels disappointed. The feeling that lies behind that is that he no longer has his favoured position with Mummy.

Perhaps now we can understand how a child who wants to put food in his stomach feels when that food does not come. The child feels that he has been removed from his special position with his mother. The food, like the boyfriend, has gone to someone else. But when the food does arrive, we can expect an overreaction—the feeling now becomes one of greed, of devouring everything.

Johnson defines *disappoint* as "to defeat of expectation," and *disappointment* as "miscarriage of expectation." In a situation where disappointment occurs, a state of expectation has existed, and that expectation has not been met.

Many times a woman has told me that she has been jilted, that she feels disappointed, and then begins to overeat because of a gnawing emptiness in the pit of her stomach. She has had, in psychological terms, her love supplies cut off. She turns to a substitute, the food, to provide love just as when she was a baby her mother supplied her with all the food and love that she required.

The prototype of this situation is a mother with her baby at her breast, supplying the baby's needs. (It may be significant in this regard that milk is used for the treatment of so many stomach conditions.)

Disappointment with oneself is also reflected in a stomach meridian energy imbalance. One may feel that he has let himself and others down, that he deserves to be demoted and has demoted himself in his own eyes.

Bitterness

A related emotional state is that of *bitterness.* The *Oxford English Dictionary* defines *bitter* as unpalatable to the mind; unpleasant and hard to "swallow" or admit. Here the facial expression differs markedly from that of disgust. With disgust, there is a downturning of the corners of the mouth, as Charles Darwin observed, "as if the child was forming a channel through which the vomit would come up from his stomach to be expelled."[28] With bitterness, the lips are often held tightly together and pursed. As we know, bitterness is the sensation we often experience just before we vomit, before we expel the food that tastes bad or is bad. It may be that this gesture of pursing the lips is an attempt to stop the vomit from coming out. Thus bitterness could be an intermediate stage between disgust and actually vomiting.[29]

In many problems involving a faulty chewing mechanism, the dentist frequently describes the problem as connected with the temporomandibular joint. With such a disturbance, there will be an impairment of the energy flow in the stomach meridian. This is compounded by the fact that the improperly chewed food is not adequately predigested in the mouth and creates difficulties of digestion when in the stomach.

We have also found that most cases of food allergies are related to impaired stomach meridian energy. We have been quite successful over the years in relieving food allergies by activating the stomach meridian using the appropriate affirmations and reinforcing with the thymus affirmations.

In the context of this meridian, how appropriate it is when we speak of "bitter disappointment."

Greed

When we feel we are not receiving enough from others, or when we have been disappointed many times in the past and those same disappointments crop up again, we turn to a source of gratification and try to take all that we can get, or all there is. With the greedy person, it is as if he is never sure the next meal will come, so he overeats at this meal and hoards all he can get.

Hanna Segal states that greed "aims at the possession of all the goodness that can be extracted from the object, regardless of the consequences."[30] Despite the effects of overeating on the greedy person, he will continue to do so. It may even reach the point where he takes what another needs just to satisfy his own desires. The greedy person feels, in essence, "I have been disappointed before. The milk was cut off when I needed it. Now, while it is flowing, I am going to take all I can and store it inside me like a camel, prepared for the next trip in the desert, because I don't know when it may be cut off again." He says this in the same emotional state that we have all experienced when we have hoarded gasoline during acute energy crises. During such times we see motorists stopping to fill up when they need only one or two gallons—they want to be safe, to have a full tank when the crunch comes.

The word *greed* comes from the root *gher*, meaning to like and to want. This became in Old English *graedig*, hungry, from which we derive our present word *greedy*. Remember that greed is not hunger. There is a cartoon in an early *Punch* of a lord seated at his dining table while his butler is bringing in a very large meal. He says to the butler, "I'm not hungry, but thank God I'm greedy."

With stomach meridian problems in general, one of the most common attempts to correct the imbalance is the seeking of gratification by food. The individual attempts to overcome his stress by oral gratification. As Theodor Reik wrote, "Excessive intake of food has the function of consolation and compensation for those emotional frustrations ."[31] This applies in particular to disappointment or deprivation. Most compulsive overeaters will readily admit that they are not hungry, but that they cannot resist the craving for food. Reik goes on to say that this greed is an exaggerated defense to ward off the anxiety of starving. He says, "that elementary fear can be put into the formula: Eat or you will starve."

Of course, greed need not be expressed in overeating. Any excessive taking in—of food, clothing, objects, any excessive accumulation—is a manifestation of greed and stomach—meridian energy imbalance. Melanie Klein in *Envy and Gratitude* stated that "greed is an impetuous and insatiable craving, exceeding what the subject needs and what the object is able and willing to give. At the unconscious level, greed aims primarily at completely scooping out, sucking dry, and devouring."

There is frequently a considerable hint of aggression in greed. A very greedy baby may almost, it seems, attack the breast to suck as much as it can—to the point where the vigour of the sucking hurts the mother. A greedy person may attempt to satisfy his own desires with little thought of the consequences to others or even to himself.

Nations can be guilty of greed. I read that the Boer War was conducted primarily out of a motive of greed. Over a hundred thousand people were killed to gain possession of the South African gold mines.

Emptiness

People who have been disappointed will often state that they feel *empty*. Empty has been defined as "needing nourishment; hungry." Hence the baby who needs more from his mother. In the *American Heritage Dictionary* we find empty defined as "void of content." Now the word "content" as a noun means "that which is contained in a receptacle"—and thus when we see empty described as "void of content," it can be taken in both senses—content as the noun and as the adjective.

Deprivation

Deprivation implies a dispossession or a loss. It is defined by one dictionary as "to depose from office." Thus you can see how it relates to disappointment. It is no wonder that both of these emotional states relate to the stomach meridian.

The origin of the word is very interesting. In Latin *de* means completely. *Privus* means private or individual. The Latin *privatus* meant "free from office." I am reminded here of a politician who has been dispossessed of his elected office by the people.

The origin is also of considerable significance. The I-E root *per* had the sense of *forward* and this gave rise to *prei-wo*, which meant forward from the rest—isolated from the others, on one's own, not part of the crowd. We say to ourselves that our private thoughts are those which are not shared with anyone else—they are separate and belong just to us. When we have been dispossessed we have been separated from that involvement and isolated from it.

The word *deprivation* is frequently used in present-day psychology, particularly in the phrase "maternal deprivation," which was coined by John Bowlby, an English psychoanalyst, to describe the psychological trauma that young children went through when separated from their mothers, especially by hospitalisation. This he saw had very definite stages and was a clinical syndrome."[32] It is now clear that the symptoms of maternal deprivation can occur apart from the hospital setting and to some extent are contributing factors in most childhood psychological illnesses. They may initiate weaknesses that could affect a person throughout his life.

Thus we see how beautifully and precisely deprivation relates to the stomach meridian—the meridian that is primarily related to receiving love and food from the mother. It is the meridian of sucking, so when we are deprived by the mother it means we are removed from the sucking situation, we are separated from our "love supplies," and we feel a sense of loss, we feel dispossessed, we feel deposed—and disappointed. It is not surprising that the positive emotional attitude for this is one of contentment, of receiving enough from mother. We feel, in essence, that "she has given me enough to sustain me mentally and physically through my activities. Through her love she has nurtured me. I am content."

Nausea

People who often suffer from nausea and stomach meridian problems may describe themselves as feeling psychologically nauseated by something. The origin of *nausea* is very interesting. It comes from the Greek *naus*, from which we get, among other words, *nautical* and *nausea*, in its original meaning referring to seasickness. The *Oxford English Dictionary* describes nausea as a feeling of sickness, with loathing of food and an inclination to vomit. It also is a strong feeling of disgust. What we do not like the taste of tends to nauseate us—physiologically and psychologically.

Hunger

Perhaps the best definition of *hunger* is a "strong desire, or craving." Initially, in both the history of the word and our own individual development, hunger applied to a need for nourishment and the uneasy or painful sensation caused by the want of food. Later it became more generalised in its use and was applied to any strong desire or craving.

Initially our hungers were physical hungers for our mothers' milk, to satisfy the unpleasant physical sensations in the stomach, to quiet the stomach meridian. But then this also became associated with the love of the mother. We hungered not just for the food or the milk but the sensation of warmth and love that we felt when she gave it to us. Thus those who hunger for food also hunger for love and contentment. Milton, in *Paradise Lost*, put it this way:

> I content me,
> and from the sling of famine fear no harm,
> nor mind it, fed with better thoughts that feed
> my hung'ring more to do my father's will.

You will often find with those who have this hunger for love that if they say at the end of a meal, "I feel satisfied and content," they will test weak, but if they say, "I could go on eating and eating," they will test strong.

In most addicts we will find unrequited hunger and discontent. Then, when the love supplies do not come to ease the hunger and create contentment, unhappiness develops.

Contentment

The positive affirmation that on testing restores balance to the energy supply in the stomach meridian is "I am content." (This seems more effective than "I am contented," perhaps because of the different speech rhythm.)

Contentment is the major positive emotional attitude related to the stomach meridian. Bear in mind that all positive feelings related to the stomach meridian originate in the initial feeding experience at the mother's breast with the first love offerings—the milk—which the baby receives from her. (Perhaps now you realise the genius of the advertisement which depicts a certain brand of milk as coming from *contented* cows.)

The basic feeling behind the affirmation "I am content" is, "I don't have everything I want or everything that could benefit me, but I have enough. What I have is sufficient." Sir Edward Dyer said,

> Content to live, this is my stay;
> I seek no more than may suffice.

Thus the person who overeats, the person who is not satisfied, is not *contented* with what he has. He is always trying for more.

When saying the positive affirmation "I am content, we might be reminded of the saying, "A contented mind is a continual feast." Here again we see the relationship between contentment and eating. In fact the word *contentment* comes from the Latin *continere*, which means to contain. We may think of the stomach itself as a container.

In the Bible we read, "I have learned, in whatsoever state I am, therewith to be content." (Philippians 4:11) Contentment is a state of oral satisfaction, of having received enough—enough love from the mother, enough love from the significant people around us. It is accepting that even though we would like to have more, we have enough now, and for that we are thankful. The writer to the Hebrews (13:5) suggested "Let your conversation be without covetousness; and be content with such things as ye have."

As we mentioned previously, food allergies are a very common clinical finding. It will be found on simple testing that certain foods deplete the life energy, and it has been my experience that in nearly every case of food allergy the meridian involved is the stomach meridian. If the positive affirmation is stated while eating, the effects of the food allergy will usually be reduced.

A great deal of modern advertising affects individuals through the stomach meridian. When we view ads we often become discontented with our lot. We don't think we have enough, so we will attempt to have more and more. Study advertisements for yourself and have someone test their effects on you. Cheek whether you feel disappointed with your lot, or discontent because your life is not like the life depicted in the ad. You may find that you will become more and more provoked, discontented, as you continue to examine these ads.

An article entitled "The Me Degeneration" begins with the following:

> Maurice Sendak once wrote a story of a pampered dog who had her own pillows, comb and brush, a red wool sweater, two windows to look out of, two bowls to eat from, and a master who loved her. Despite this she left home, explaining, "I am discontented. I want something I do not have. There must be more to life than having everything!"[33]

Tranquil

Another interesting finding in our research is that the stress induced in an individual by noise affects the stomach meridian. The noise of city traffic or general unnecessary clatter will often upset the energy balance in the stomach meridian. The positive affirmation, "I am tranquil," often causes a weak stomach meridian test point to test strong. *Tranquil* comes from the same source as *quiet. Shakespeare (in Othello)* recognised the relationship between contentment and tranquillity when he wrote, "Farewell the Tranquill minde; farewell Content."

The test point for the thyroid meridian. One-third down an imaginary line between the umbilicus and symphysis pubis.

Thyroid Meridian*

The meridian of hope

Thyroid	Lightness Buoyancy
	Heaviness Depression

Negative Emotions: Depression
                      Despair
                      Grief
                      Hopelessness
                      Despondency
                      Loneliness
                      Solitude

Positive Affirmations: I am light and buoyant.
                          I am buoyed up with hope.

Test Image: You are at home, you have no energy, and
               you have nothing to do worth doing. You
               feel heavy and weighed down. Everything
               is just too much.

Depression

Depression is the predominant negative emotion related to the thyroid meridian. There is a great deal of argument and controversy regarding what is actually meant by depression, and many learned psychiatric tomes have been written on this subject. To me it is quite simple.

For many years I compiled a list of the symptoms reported to me by patients when they felt depressed. All of them seemed to imply that they were literally being pushed or pressed or sometimes pulled down—de-pressed. For example, they would describe themselves as being low or flat, as if there were a weight on their backs. They would sometimes say that they just felt too heavy to move, they just did not have enough energy to raise themselves

* Classically called the Triple Heater meridian

Most people will test weak for the thyroid meridian when looking at this photo. Saying the positive affirmation for the thyroid meridian will overcome the weakness.

out of a chair. This is what we mean by depression. Of course, it can be very mild. We often feel "depressed" on those days when everything is just too much—just too much effort to get up and begin the day. Our load seems too heavy for us to carry.

Stokes refers to "a fit of the blues" as "a depression over loss." Indeed, many depressed patients report that they seem to be "in a blue funk" or "crying the blues" or "down in the dumps."

The writer of Psalm 69:20 referred to depression when he wrote,

> Reproach hath broken my heart;
> And I am full of heaviness:

The positive affirmation for this feeling is the sensation of being light, buoyant, and floating. The psychiatric opposite state of depression is that of elation, "being lifted up out of." Thus we find that when the thyroid meridian tests weak, if the person says, "I am light and buoyant," and imagines himself as being light and buoyant, then he will test strong.

The thyroid meridian is the continuum of mass—it relates to our self-concept of our own mass. In clinical practice, mild cases of underactivity of the thyroid gland are very, very common. I would estimate that at least 70 percent of the patients I see in my practice have some evidence of underactive thyroid. One of the more subtle tests, and one you can perform yourself, is to take your temperature every morning before rising. The thermometer should be used under the arm and kept there for ten minutes. A normal reading is between 97.6°F. and 98.2°F. If it is generally lower than this, it usually indicates low thyroid activity. It will be found that as the thyroid activity increases to normal, the morning temperature will rise. It is no wonder that most hypothyroid people describe themselves as being most tired and heavy in the morning, because this is when their temperature is at its lowest. The thyroid gland may be seen, in a way, as the body's thermostat. If the temperature is turned down, there will be underactivity.

Frequently it will be found that people whose thyroid meridian tests weak generally tilt their heads to the side. A classic example is that of the Botticelli *Venus*. Often you will find that as the person corrects his head and neck posture, the thyroid meridian will test strong. You may recall that this gesture of tilting the head is often employed, as in the *Venus*, by artists when they wish to transmit the message that the female in the portrait is a dependent waif who requires our nurturing to survive. When a woman tilts her head to the side in this manner it often brings out maternal or paternal feelings in us. We wish to be her protector.

Thyroid meridian weakness often occurs when there is a double-bind.[34] Whenever you find that you or your friend have an underactive thyroid meridian, think "I am in two minds at the moment about the most important person or thing in my life. I predominantly like the situation but I am in two minds about it." (You are one step away from the basic positive thymus attitude.)

The double-bind situation may be related to the fact that very often we find that people whose thyroid meridian tests weak wear glasses. This may be because their refractive errors and often their central problems with reading, which are more basic than the refractive errors (by this I mean the subtle dyslexias that so many of these people have), are from the same source. When they are reading, they are not quite sure what they are reading. It is as if they are in two minds about what they have read. They have a central processing problem and in this state they often tilt their heads so as to try to read or see better. Although it is not invariably the case, you will more likely than not find that people who tend to tilt their heads and people who wear glasses will, at some level, have a thyroid meridian problem and also at some level, either conscious or unconscious, they are depressed.

We often find that men whose thyroid meridian test point tests weak on a long-term basis tend toward loss of hair and baldness, apparently related to underactivity of the thyroid gland.

Let me give you an example to bring these various concepts into focus. A male patient, although only in his early thirties, was suffering from quite severe hair loss. Each morning there would be masses of hair on his pillow, and he would lose more in the shower. His early-morning temperature was very low, about 96'F., and of numerous medications and supplements used to activate his thyroid gland, none had been successful. Of course, I asked him about his depression. He said that at times he in fact did feel very low and depressed over his relationship with his girlfriend. She was keeping him constantly in two minds. She would wax hot and then she would wane cold. Sometimes she said how much she loved him and desired him and how much she wanted to marry him, and the next time he saw her, she would say she had decided not to get married and that she did not know whether she should even see him again. This went on and on. Many evenings would be spent arguing about this, and after such an evening, he would test weak.

Eventually I said to him, "Look, this has to stop. Either she is going to continue to have a positive relationship with you or not. This 'on-again, off-again' relationship is affecting you." He exclaimed, "You're right. I'm going to explain this situation to her, and then she's going to have to make a decision and stick to it!" He telephoned me the next day and said, "I don't understand what happened. I haven't even spoken to her yet, but having made this decision I feel so much better! I am no longer depressed!" Then he said, "Miraculously, for the first time this morning, my temperature was normal and even more incredibly I didn't lose any hair last night." Since that day he has suffered no further hair loss! And the relationship is slowly but surely resolving itself to their mutual satisfaction.

I recall another patient, a woman who had been widowed for some twenty years and who suffered from a chronic, clinical low thyroid condition. She stated that she had been depressed for many years, ever since her husband had died. I asked her when she had started to tilt her head (it was now permanently tilted, it seemed, at quite a severe angle). She said she couldn't remember, but when I asked her daughter, her daughter readily volunteered, "She started that almost the day after my father died." As she underwent treatment, I noticed that as her depression lifted and her thyroid functioning improved, she no longer tilted her head as she had previously.

Incidentally, most flute players tilt their heads. It has been my finding that nearly all of them have some degree of thyroid underactivity, and they also tend to be depressed.

You will find, not surprisingly, that when you look at the Botticelli *Venus* your thyroid meridian will test weak. But if you move the page around such that although the head remains tilted in relationship to the body, it is angled so that the eyes are parallel to your line of vision, you will perceive that the head is no longer tilted, at least in relationship to yourself, and your thyroid meridian will test strong.

In the late 1950s, antidepressant medications were first on the market, and very good results were obtained in clinical cases of severe depression. The cases with which we worked in the early days of antidepressants were those who were called psychotic depressives, those who would otherwise have had electroshock therapy and almost invariably were confined to the hospital. However, not that high a percentage of any psychiatrist's practice, and certainly not a very high percentage of the general population, may be classified as severely depressed.

When antidepressant medications appeared, suddenly depression became respectable. Many patients who were suffering from all manner of nonpsychotic illnesses were suddenly being called "depressed." They were said to be suffering from the disease of "depression" for a number of reasons. One was that we began to recognise depression in milder forms than had been customary, which was a very valuable "preventive" measure. Second, we now had a nice clinical label we could put on all these poor miserable people who had no "diagnosis" before. Furthermore, we had something that we could give them. They had never responded to barbiturates nor to tranquillisers (because they basically were neither anxious nor schizophrenic). The psychiatrists were always looking for the magic pill. And so, through subtle reorientation of thoughts based both on the general trends of their own professional societies and the drug house advertising, gradually the antidepressant drugs were dispensed to people who were not clinically depressed. The sales of antidepressant medication skyrocketed, a trend that has continued. More importantly, more and more people were being called "depressed." Depression was "in." It was suddenly not an epithet to be depressed. It was an accepted clinical state.

It is important to realise that the vast majority of people who feel depressed and test weak at the thyroid meridian are not suffering from clinical depression. Certainly not everyone who has a thyroid meridian weakness should take an antidepressant drug.

We see, then, that depression became acceptable, but other emotional states did not. For example, if I were writing a letter back to a patient's general practitioner, I could say, "Mr. Smith has the following symptoms . . . He is suffering from depression for which I have prescribed an antidepressant." Everyone would be satisfied, except the patient. If I had written back to the referring doctor and said, "Mr. Smith is suffering from unhappiness," the doctor would have said two things: (1) that I was not a proper doctor because unhappiness was not a medical disease, and (2) what was the good of diagnosing unhappiness anyhow, as there are no pills to cure unhappiness. For over twenty years I have watched as depression became a loosely used word, and the vast quantities of antidepressant drugs being used came about through this mechanism.

Melanie Klein describes the first stage of the psychic development of the child as the paranoid-schizoid position, and the second stage as the depressive position. The paranoid-schizoid position corresponds to the lung meridian, and the depressive position corresponds in part to the thyroid meridian. As you will see later, there is a direct relationship between the lung meridian and the thyroid meridian. Further, the lung meridian is the primary meridian, the major source through which energy enters the body—the breath. There is a development from predominantly lung meridian problems in the earliest days of life to thyroid meridian problems later. Additionally, lung meridian problems relate to the right hemisphere and thyroid meridian problems relate to the left hemisphere. Thus, there is a progression from predominantly right-hemisphere activity to predominantly left-hemisphere activity. It is only after the child has passed through the positions described by Klein that he is, in a sense, integrated, capable of seeing people as whole objects and relating to them person-to-person and really loving them. This loving state corresponds to high thymus activity, which is achieved only when there is a balance between the cerebral hemispheres, such as is achieved when the lung and thyroid meridians are balanced. Hence these findings are in essential agreement and in fact corroborate the deepest tenets of child psychoanalysis.

Melancholy

Melancholy is the state of depression.[35] In Latin, *melancholia* means literally "the condition of having black bile." The *Oxford English Dictionary* points out that "In early references its prominent symptoms are ... propensity to causeless and violent anger [that is, wrath]" and in later references mental gloom and sadness. In the lighter sense, it is used as tender or pensive sadness, for example, as in the song, "Come to me, my melancholy baby"—"baby" being tearful and in need of cuddling, hardly the state of a true melancholic.

As early as 1485, melancholy was defined as depression of spirits, a condition of gloom or dejection. In "Mourning and Melancholia," Freud wrote that the first distinguishing mental feature of melancholia was a profoundly painful dejection. The "propensity to causeless and violent anger" is more in keeping with the choleric (see page 42-44) state, that of yellow bile; whereas the state of depression is in keeping with the black bile, melancholia.

Both *choler* and *gall* are derived from the Indo-European root *ghel.* Its original meaning was "to shine" and referred to bright materials, for example, "yellow metal," from which we get *gold* and yellow liquid, the *bile.* (Other words from this root include glimmer, *glisten, glitter, glee, glad,* and *glow.*)

Despair

Despair means the loss of all hope. The Latin *sperare* means to hope. It is derived from the Indo-European root *spei,* which meant to thrive or prosper. As it has been said, despair, hopelessness, depression, despondency, and dejection denote "emotional states marked by lowness of spirit." Incidentally, *spirit* is derived from the same root. (See pages 4-5)

Grief

Another powerful negative emotional state related to the thyroid meridian is that of *grief.* Grief comes from the same word as *grave,* and likewise means heavy. It is not surprising that in psychological literature grief is closely related to depression and the stage of mourning after the loss of a loved one. The Greek word *baros,* means heaviness and comes from the same basic root, and from this we get *barometer*—an instrument that measures the heaviness of the air.

In this context we may find new implications in job 6:2—"Oh that my grief were thoroughly weighed."

Hopelessness

Another negative emotional attitude associated with the thyroid meridian is *hopelessness.* The positive state, of course, is *hope,* which is thought possibly to have been derived from the same source as hop—quoting Eric Partridge, "the basic idea would be a leaping, or to leap, with expectation."[36] With hope you have the feeling of being lifted up, of being light and buoyant, of rising above the burdens that are pushing you down. Hence the best affirmation is "I am buoyed up with hope."

Let me give you an example of how being in two minds affects the thyroid meridian energy and relates to depression. I recently saw a priest who had been suffering from a severe depression for many years. He was very lethargic, very tired, always feeling that he was "down" and "low" and had no energy, no thought for the future, no hope whatsoever; he had frequently contemplated suicide. Upon testing we found thyroid meridian weakness. I explained to him what this meant, and I talked to him about how hope would overcome his feelings of depression. I told him that I had often found that people who tended to have thyroid meridian problems were those who tended to be in two minds about everything.

When he came back a week later he said, "You know, I feel so much better! I have been saying to myself, 'I have hope, I am light and buoyant.' And I think what is helping me most is this idea of being in two minds. For example, every time I meet a woman and talk to her, I seem to be in two minds. Not about sex, but about whether I should be close with a person of the opposite sex." He said, "I can see myself being in two minds about this all the time. I don't know exactly how to handle it completely yet, but you were so right to bring it up. Ever since I recognized it last week, I have felt so much better."

So I said, "Well, let's find out if you really do want to have a relationship with a woman or not." He said, "There have been two women in my life recently. One is Vivienne, and the other is Laura." Then I told him to phrase his question very precisely, which he did, and he said, "I want to see more of Laura." And he tested strong. When he said, "I don't want to see Laura any more," he tested weak. And with Vivienne it was reversed. He said, "I wouldn't have thought that originally, but now that we see it with the test results I can easily understand and accept that that is the case. So what happens now?"

I then showed him that since he had been thinking in terms of hope and had begun to deal with his dilemma regarding the women, his thyroid meridian tested strong. But his kidney meridian tested weak. So I said to him, "Now that you have solved the question about whether or not to see these women, the next question is whether you wish to initiate a sexual relationship." At this point he said, "Obviously I am not ready for that question yet. Why don't we just hold it in abeyance." When he said the positive affirmation for the kidney meridian, "My sexual energies are balanced," he tested strong.

We then discussed the fact that over the next few months we would deal with the macrocosm of his problem. As he overcomes his two-mindedness about intimacy, in the social sense of the word, with women, and as he overcomes his depression, then he is going to have the obvious question: "Will I have a sexual relationship with her or not?" This, too, can be examined and resolved.

Despondency

The *Oxford English Dictionary* calls *despondency* depression or dejection (*dejection* means literally a throwing down) of spirits. It is distinguished from *despair* as not expressing entire hopelessness but a loss of hope. Someone who is despondent may be described as "labouring under mental depression."

While it is tempting to link *despondent* with *ponderous* and thus associate it with the idea of heaviness, which relates to the thyroid meridian, this is not etymologically the case. Despondent derives rather from *spondere,* to promise, which also gives rise to *respond. De-* is used in the sense of away from; hence in the sense of giving up, losing. The Greek *sponde* was a drink offering, a solemn truce used when making a treaty, for example, to promise. Thus *despond* means to abandon, to lose; to fall away from one's aspirations and hopes and desires, and perhaps then to sink into a depression.

Loneliness

Nancy and Wayne have been married for twenty years. They are deeply devoted to each other and very close, perhaps more so because they have no children. Each day, Nancy can hardly wait for Wayne to come home from work. If he is even a little late, she becomes apprehensive. And every evening she is there to greet him with her broad smile. It seems so very idyllic, but there is another side to it. Nancy feels terribly lonely all day and, in fact, has felt like that ever since the first day after their honeymoon when she found herself alone in their home.

As soon as Wayne leaves in the morning Nancy turns on the radio, not to hear the news or to listen to music but for the people that come into her room through the radio. She says, "I listen to Carlton Fredericks and Joyce Brothers and all the others." These are her company during the day. She says if she ever turns off the radio, she talks to herself. She cannot bear to be alone. She feels lonely all day. She wants Wayne or somebody with her all the time, so in her mind she creates other people. She often imagines that other people are in the room with her. And when she turns on the radio or talks to herself, she is also imagining that there is some-one else there.

Sometimes when this loneliness becomes overbearing and pulls her down, Nancy becomes a closet drinker, often making toasts to the guests in her mind whom she believes she is entertaining. So each day, in spite of the beauty and the comfort of her home, is a day of loneliness and dejection. Her need for her husband to come home is not just out of love, but because she knows that this will relieve the terrible loneliness.

I remember once I suggested to the two of them that to ease some of the business pressure on him he should come home for lunch, as his office was not very far away. Nancy jumped to her feet and clapped her hands in joy and giggled like a child. I realised then just how lonely she was and what a lift this would give her.

Now she is a great deal better. In part this is because for the first time she has openly admitted that she is lonely and that this is why she drinks during the day. Whereas Wayne had always thought that Nancy's great need for him and to be with him at all times was out of love, now he sees that it was also out of loneliness. This did not cause him to love her any less, but to be more sympathetic toward her. He calls her up from work several times a day and he comes home for lunch when he can.

One of Nancy's chief aids has been to reaffirm the thyroid affirmation, "I am light and floating," every morning as soon as he leaves. And whenever she feels lonely she affirms , I am light and floating." Nancy still prefers to have Wayne with her, but now she can be on her own without having to turn on the radio or imagining that other people are with her.

We suffer so much from this fear of being alone. As P. G. Hamerton says, "Woe unto him that is never alone, and cannot bear to be alone. Who must hang on because of the fear of loneliness, of the fear of being by oneself, alone, naked with themselves and with God."

Loneliness comes from the Old English *an*, meaning one, which in Middle English becomes *al one*, meaning all (that is, utterly) alone, from which we get *lonely*. The *Oxford English Dictionary* describes *lonely* as being dejected arising from want of company or society; having a feeling of solitariness; being "quite by oneself, unaccompanied."

One can be alone but not lonely. With the latter there is the sense of dejection (literally "thrown down"), but one need not be adversely affected by being alone. In fact, it may be welcome. We can say that the pathological reaction to the state of being on one's own is that particular feeling of dejection from the hurt of separation, and this we call *loneliness.*

Solitude

Solitude comes from the Latin *solus*, meaning alone. It can be seen as a positive or negative state. It is "the state of being or living alone," which in itself does not imply any form of depression or dejection. It is also defined as a state of loneliness. In that sense, Lady Montagu wrote, "your letters ... are the only pleasures of my solitude ."[37]

On the other hand, solitude can be a great virtue, as Aldous Huxley says, "The most powerful and original mind, the more it will incline towards the religion of solitude."And Henry Thoreau says in *Walden*, "I never found a companion that was so companionable as solitude."

The answer to solitude and loneliness is never to feel alone, but to welcome the time of quiet and of aloneness. Epictetus in his *Discourses* says, "When you have closed your doors, and darkened your room, remember never to say you are alone, for you are not alone. God is within." And perhaps Cicero said it best when he said, "I am never less alone than when alone."

Hope

Hope is "the expectation of something desired; desire combined with expectation." The therapeutic powers of hope have long been recognised. For example, Sophocles wrote, "It is hope that maintains most of mankind."Also, Cowley, "Hope! Of all ills that men endure, / The only cheap and universal cure."

In *The Art of Preserving Health,* John Armstrong pointed out the therapeutic advantages of hope but also contrasted them with the basic negative emotion of fear: "Our greatest good, and what we least can spare, Is hope: the last of all our evils, fear."

The idea of hope as being uplifting and helping to overcome our depressed, pushed-down spirits, is best stated simply by Milton: "Hope elevates."

Elation is the opposite of the state of depression. Depression is being pushed down, elation is being lifted up out of (Latin *e*, out, and *latus*, carried; hence *elatus*, carried away or lifted up). And so elation is defined as "being uplifted, elevation of spirits, buoyancy.

Small Intestine Meridian

The meridian of joy

Small Intestine	Joy
	Sorrow Sadness

Negative Emotions:	Sadness Sorrow
Positive Affirmations:	I am full of joy. I am jumping with joy.
Test Image:	You feel full of tears, as if you could cry.

Sadness

The predominant negative emotional attitude for the small intestine meridian is sadness. It is difficult to describe this word precisely. The root is *sa,* to satisfy, which became in Latin *sat,* meaning enough, from which we derive *sated, satisfied, and saturate.* In Old English, *sad* meant serious, discreet, sober, heavy, dark, solid. The oldest meaning was that of sated.[38] Sad is often used in the sense of being full: having one's fill. It would suggest that its original meaning was "full of food," which has come to mean "fed up." Stokes says that "sad" once indicated satiety, then resoluteness.

The "fed up" connotation may well be significant in that the small intestine receives all food passed on from the stomach. Perhaps when energy supplied to the small intestine is inadequate, it will remain gorged and full of food, not being able to digest it and pass it on.

My psychiatric experience has led me to feel that sadness means full—of tears. I know that whenever I see someone who seems like he could cry, and I say to him, "Are you feeling sad?" then he starts

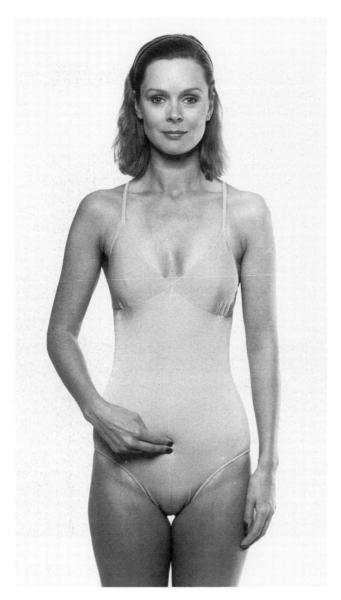

The test point for the small intestine meridian. Two-thirds down an imaginary line between the umbilicus and symphysis pubis.

Most people will test weak for the small intestine meridian when looking at this photo. Saying the positive affirmation for the small intestine meridian will overcome the weakness.

to cry. Sometimes he will say, "I'm glad you said that because I just couldn't get it out. But I was up to here with tears." And he will generally point to his cheeks, just below his eyes. So it seems that sadness may be when we have had enough, when we are fed up, when we are full of tears, but just unable to express them. The Psalmist expressed his thanks in Psalm 116:8. "For thou hast delivered ... mine eyes from tears."

Milton said, "The Angelic Guards ascended, mute and sad for Man."

Sorrow

The related negative emotion for the small intestine is *sorrow.* The roots for sorrow in the Indo-European languages seem to relate to physical pain and suffering.

The relationship between sorrow and crying is best expressed by Jean Ingelow: "When sparrows build and the leaves break forth, My old sorrow wakes and cries." And Thomas Moore, "Weep on! And as thy sorrows flow, / I'll taste the luxury of woe." Johnson says, "Sorrow is not commonly understood as the effect of present evil, but of lost good." In other words, crying over spilt milk.

Through our testing techniques, we can differentiate between emotional states and consequently the words used to describe them. Even dictionaries may not be as accurate. For example, sorrow may be "an instance or cause of grief or sadness." We can test for ourselves and show that sorrow, like sadness, relates to the small intestine meridian, whereas grief relates to the thyroid meridian. These emotional states of sorrow and sadness are related to, but are quite distinct from, grief.

Keats gives us an example of the relationship between sorrow and tears:

> She nothing said, but, pale and meek,
> And rose and knelt before him,
> Wept a rain of sorrows at his words.

And Pope wrote, "Down his right beard a stream of sorrow flows." Shakespeare also has the same idea connecting sorrow and tears:

> Where they view'd each others sorrow,
> Sorrow that friendly sighs sought still to dry.

Joy

Both of the negative emotional states related to the small intestine meridian have to do with tears. The positive emotional states that corresponds to the small intestine meridian is joy. The primitive root from which it is derived is *gau*, to rejoice, from which we get in Latin, *gaudium*, which meant gladness or delight. This gave rise in English to *gaudy*, and possibly to the French, *jouer*, to play.

Joy has been thought of as high pleasure or delight. "The joy of the heart makes the face merry." And in Job 41:22 we find a phrase that expresses the continuum of the small intestine meridian: "Sorrow is turned into joy before him."

Note that the *Oxford English Dictionary* calls joy "a vivid emotion of pleasure, arising from a sense of well-being or satisfaction." Here we are reminded of the opposite, sad, which originally meant sated or satisfied.

I remember very clearly a female student who tested weak for this meridian. When I told her what the weakness implied she burst into tears and cried and cried. She eventually was able to compose herself and said that she had been thinking only that morning about how sad she felt because God had not given her a more beautiful body. This, she felt, was the reason that she had never been able to marry. I reminded her of the quotation from Coverdale: "They that sowe in teers, shall reape in joye." She used the positive affirmation for some time and reported a great improvement in her emotional state. She told me that it has really helped her to come to grips with her dissatisfied feelings about her body.

It is wonderful that now we can determine exactly which emotional states are troubling us and then to know exactly, precisely what words and what thoughts can correct them. Before, when a patient cried, or when anyone cried, I did not know the precise emotion that was affecting him. I certainly did not know what would be the most comforting words for me to say or that he could say to help himself. But now I know, for example, that when someone is crying, it would be best for him to think of joy, because joy is the antidote to tears. Now when someone is crying, my thoughts are, "How can I help him turn his tears of sadness to tears of joy?"[39] This is transmutation.

The test point for the bladder meridian. Just above symphysis pubis.

Bladder Meridian

The meridian of peace and harmony

Bladder	*Peace, Harmony*
	Restlessness, Impatience

Negative Emotions:	Restlessness Impatience Frustration
Positive Affirmations:	I am at peace. I am in harmony. Dissonances and conflicts within me have been resolved. I am balanced.
Test Image:	You are caught in a traffic jam. The bus is moving very, very slowly. You are in a great hurry to get home. You are becoming very upset.

Restlessness, Impatience, and Frustration

The predominant emotional states affecting the energy balance in the bladder meridian are *restlessness, impatience,* and *frustration.* Have you ever seen a little boy as he becomes restless and impatient? Sometimes he will hold his genitals as if to prevent himself from urinating. I am sure you know of people who, when they get restless, have to go to the bathroom frequently but they pass only small quantities of urine each time. These are often people who quickly become restless and often shake their legs when they do. They have great difficulty in being settled and at peace. They have in essence what is termed a "nervous bladder."

Johnson defined *restless* as "without peace." His dictionary states that the word was also used in the sense of being "not still."

Frustration comes from the Latin *frustare,* meaning to drag things out. It is related to the Latin adverb, *frustra,* in vain. Again

Most people will test weak for the bladder meridian when looking at this photo. Saying the positive affirmation for the bladder meridian will overcome the weakness.

we have the idea of being held back from achieving our goals. There seems to be a similarity between the quality of patient endurance and frustration as a result of things being dragged out. From the Latin we learn that a thing may be dragged out to the point where the action becomes useless (in vain). In our test image, we can imagine the bus as being jammed in traffic for so long that our purpose has been thwarted.

Patience

Patience has been called the capacity of calm endurance. When on the motionless bus in our test image, this is the very quality we have such difficulty in experiencing.

The primitive root from which patience is derived is *pei*, to hurt, from which we get in Latin *pati*, to suffer. The implication is the ability to suffer something over a period of time. Hence, calm endurance. Impatience, then, is the inability to endure with calm until the goal may be reached: Pepys wrote in his diary that he was "much impatient by these few days sickness." In *Troilus and Cressida* we find the sentence, "There is between my will and all offences a guard of patience." We also find it said that, "Endurance is nobler than strength, and patience than beauty." Back in 1560 Thomas Wilson wrote, "Patience is a remedy for every disease."

Peace

Shakespeare, in *Henry IV*, beautifully hinted at the basic concept of peace:

A peace is of the nature of a conquest;
For then both parties nobly are subdued,
And neither party loser.

The root from which *peace* comes is *pag*, meaning to fasten or to join. This becomes in Latin, *pace, peace*. This also gives rise to the English word *pact*, meaning an agreement.

We can conceptualise peace as occurring after a pact has been established between the warring parts within ourselves. In our test image, for example, part of us wants to get home as quickly as possible, and nothing else seems to matter at the moment except that. There are desires and wishes within each of us that we are striving to achieve, and yet we are being frustrated in reaching our goals. Inside us there develops a turmoil, with parts fighting other parts. When these internal factions come to an agreement with each other, sign a pact, in effect, then there will be internal peace.

In Job 22:21 we find: "Acquaint now thyself with him, and be at peace; thereby good shall come unto thee."

Harmony

Another positive emotional state related to the bladder meridian is *harmony*, which means "an agreement in feeling." This is when all the separate parts join together for the ultimate good of all. When there is peace and harmony, there can be progress. Harmony has been described as a "combination ... of parts ... so as to form a consistent and orderly whole; agreement."

We find that the root behind harmony is *ar*, which means to fit together, to form a cohesive whole—in other words, to be at peace.

In *Henry VI,* Shakespeare wrote:

> How irksome is this music to my heart!
> When such strings jar what hope of harmony?

When there is internal discord and imbalance, there is no internal peace and no harmony.

In musical terms, harmony has been described as the resolution of dissonance. This might apply equally as well to ourselves—mind, body, and spirit.

Byron said, "Where all is harmony, and calm and quiet."

Serenity

Serenity, another positive emotional attribute associated with the bladder meridian, comes from the Latin *serenis,* which usually was used to refer to the sky and the weather. When it was serene, it was clear and peaceful. This is probably related to the word *serus*, meaning "of the evening," from which we get the French word *soir.* From the same source as serenity we also have *serenade.*

Serenity means clear, fine, and calm. The original root was *ksero*, which meant dry—referring to a clear, calm, dry day or evening—a time of serenity, peace, and harmony.

Calm

Calm is another positive emotional attitude related to the bladder meridian. The most pleasing history of the word *calm* is that in the Provençal language the related word *chaume* signifies "the time when the flocks rest." This is a time of peace and harmony. The Greek word from which this comes, *kauma*, refers to "the heat of the day, when beasts are at rest, winds fallen, the fields quiet."

We so often find that restless people have, on testing, an energy imbalance associated with the bladder meridian. We then go over the positive words to be used in their affirmations, and they often state that they think of a serenade, or a peaceful day with the flocks resting in the field, and the like. With this visualisation, they test strong.

Conception and Governing Vessels

These two meridians are not primarily organ-related, although it is thought that the governing vessel supplies life energy to the brain. The conception vessel and the governing vessel are more the collectors of energy that has already passed through the organ/meridian system. The test points are illustrated on pages 110 and 112. For the conception vessel the point is slightly below the midpoint of the lower lip, and for the governing vessel it is in the intermaxillary suture at a point one third of the distance from the anterior nasal spine to the midpoint of the upper lip.

The emotional attitudes associated with these meridians are not in the same category as guilt, for example, nor are they basic emotions such as love and hate. These are more what we might term second-order emotions and, while it is significant to find them on testing, they rarely require specific individual correction. They tend to correct themselves when the associated underlying emotional state is itself corrected.

Governing Vessel

The negative emotional state associated with the governing vessel is *embarrassment*. I have attempted for some time without success to find out how the origin of the word *embarrassment*

The test point for the governing vessel meridian. Slightly above the midpoint of the upper lip.

relates to its present usage. It comes from the Latin *barra*, which means a bar, so to embarrass means literally to impede or to put in bars. Perhaps the meaning, although this is merely my own interpretation, implies the situation in which someone is imprisoned and put on display, as in a stockade, for something he has done wrong. The negative visualisation, or test image, in everyday life would be something such as to imagine that you are walking down a very busy street and suddenly realise that your fly is undone, or that your wraparound skirt has blown open.

You will find that this meridian's imbalance may transiently appear when another meridian problem is disclosed. For example, a person may reveal a sexual indecision (kidney meridian), and as soon as this is dealt with, he may then show a governing vessel weakness—that is, embarrassment because someone else knows of his sexual indecision.

Conception Vessel

The conception vessel has to do with *shame*. The negative visualisation, or test image, would be to imagine that you have just been caught and accused of a crime, such as theft. You may recall that when we discussed the eytmology of the word *hate*, we showed that the root *kar*, which meant to like or desire, also gave rise to *kam*, which meant to cover over, from which we derived in English *chemise* and *shame*. There has long been the idea of covering ourselves in shame, hence the saying "naked and unashamed." We literally use our chemise to cover our shame. When we blush with shame, everyone can see that we have done something wrong. We have been caught in the act. Shame is, in a sense, the public display, the public awareness, of what we feel is our "sin." Shame, like embarrassment, will be cleared up as we overcome our feelings about the "sin." One is reminded here of the expressions "to be shamefaced," and, of course, "Oh shame! Where is thy blush?" In Isaiah 47:3 we read, "Thy nakedness shall be uncovered, yea, thy shame shall be seen."

Johnson defines shame as "the passion felt when reputation is supposed to be lost; the passion expressed sometimes by blushes."

Anthropologists have related that in primitive cultures the time the child learns the word *shame* is when he begins to cover his genitals. One of the beauties of our work with language and

The test point for the conception vessel. Slightly below the midpoint of the lower lip.

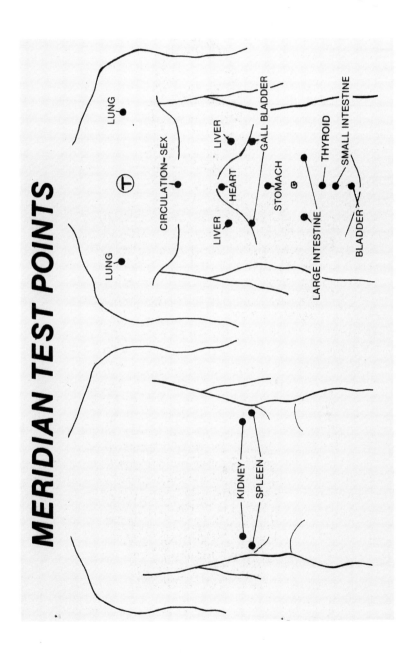

MERIDIAN TEST POINTS

LUNG
LUNG
CIRCULATION—SEX
LIVER
LIVER
HEART
STOMACH
GALL BLADDER
LARGE INTESTINE
THYROID
SMALL INTESTINE
BLADDER
KIDNEY
SPLEEN

psychological states is the discovery of a fact such as this: shame, chemise, and shirt all have the same origin. Here we see how, through the ages, the psychological concept and a physical correlate of that concept are still related in our psyches; this we can learn from present-day psychological techniques. Then, on investigating the history of the words, we find that they came from the same source. What we discover today psychologically, the etymologist can discover through his discipline. Words that are connected at their root are connected even today, and those distant roots are connected in our psyches.

Shyness also is a negative attitude relating to the conception vessel. This may imply that shy people are often those who hide themselves lest their shame be seen. This connection between shame and shyness has previously been pointed out by Sydney Smith, "The most curious offspring of shame is shyness."

Bernard Shaw in *Man and Superman* says, "We live in an atmosphere of shame. We are ashamed of everything that is real about us; ashamed of ourselves, of our relatives, of our incomes, of our accidents, of our opinions, of our experience, just as we are ashamed of our naked skins."

Perhaps the timidity and the distrust which are so characteristic of shyness are a result of a fear of punishment—the "sin" has been revealed through the shame.

There are many references to shame that imply public display. From Shakespeare, King John, "You but make it blush, and glow with shame of your proceedings, Hubert." Edward Spenser in The *Faerie Queene,* "Relenting Sorrow did in darkenesse lye, / and Shame his ugly face did hide from the living eye."

As Darwin wrote in *The Expression of the Emotions of Animals and Man*, "Under a keen sense of shame, there is a strong desire for concealment." And in Jeremiah 51:51 we read, "Shame hath covered our faces."

Summary of Testing Techniques

The testing process is far from difficult. In fact, it is incredibly simple, and is now being carried out by thousands of doctors and lay people. However, it requires experience and practice to do it accurately and reliably. The procedure is:

1.   Test the thymus. If the thymus tests strong, then you know that the person's life energy is high, and he is, at the moment, invulnerable to many stresses. You need go no further in your testing because, if the thymus is testing strong, his cerebral hemispheres are balanced and he is now creative, productive, and able to solve his problems. His emotional states are balanced and neutralised and there are no major negative emotions interfering with his life energy at that time. (You have seen from the photographs how someone's looks can affect you; therefore, you must make yourself neutral when you perform the test.) *Note:* There are certain instances in which the testing can produce false positive results, that is, the subject may test strong when he really should be testing weak. In severe cases I have even found that certain people may test strong for refined sugar! They also may test strong for hateful thoughts and, paradoxically, weak for loving thoughts. These false results can easily be prevented by having the subject chew a ribonucleic acid tablet (readily available at any health-food store) just prior to the testing. (For details on this refer to "The Umbilicus Test" in my *Collected Papers,* Volume II.) While the incidence of these false positive results is not high, if you want to be absolutely sure of the results it is always best to give a tablet prior to testing. I do it routinely in my practice.

2.   If the thymus tests weak, do the *hemisphere test.* This will indicate which cerebral hemisphere is dominant at this time, and the subject will then know that certain corrective measures are required to alleviate this general imbalance.

3.   At the same time you will learn from the hemisphere test which set of meridian test points to challenge. If the person is left-hemisphere dominant, you test the "midline" meridian points; if he is right-hemisphere dominant, you test the "bilateral" points. (With the bilateral points, you usually need to test only one side. If, as occurs occasionally, you do not find anything on the initial test side, then test the other side.)

4.   Now that you have found the specific meridian weakness, simply have the person repeat several times, with feeling, and visualising the appropriate positive affirmation.

5.   Retest and you will find that the meridian is now energised, the hemispheres are balanced, the person is therefore creative, and the thymus is testing strong. The blockage of the flow of life energy has been corrected.

That is all you need to do to find out and to correct the predominant emotional state affecting anyone at the time of testing. Isn't that simple—and isn't it of vital importance?

As pointed out previously, experience and practice are required to do the testing reliably and accurately. It is simple, but it must be done precisely. There are a number of variables which must be controlled, such as whether you are standing under fluorescent lights, whether a television or radio is on while you are testing, or other environmental factors.

As an example of a hidden but important variable, consider the following incident. Amy has never really had a boyfriend, but currently has a crush on a young man in her class. In the three years that they have been in the same class he has never asked her out, so recently she summoned up all her courage and sent him a note saying that she would like to go out with him. Now she is concerned because she realises that she has been forward. She is worried that he may take her message wrong and think that she wants to have sex with him, which was not her intent. I tested her for "I like Tom" and she tested weak. I asked her to say, "I don't like Tom" and she tested strong. She protested, "But this is impossible. Of course I like him. Why else would I ask him out?" Then I remembered her concern that he may become sexually involved with her, so I asked Amy to say, "I want to have sex with Tom," and before I tested her she replied, "Of course I don't!" I felt that she was telling the truth, but she tested strong for the statement. Everything was *reversed*. She tested as not liking Tom and yet she wanted to have sex with him, the opposite of what she and I believed. Then she asked me, "Do you think the results would be different if I took off my digital watch?" Routinely I have all my students remove their digital watches before we begin any testing. But in Amy's case, I had overlooked it because it was concealed in a bracelet. After she removed the watch, the results were the opposite of those we obtained initially. She tested strong for "I like Tom" and weak when she said, "I want to have sex with Tom." We then reviewed some earlier testing and found that all the results had been reversed because of the digital watch .[40]

Another way to test for the underactive meridian is to have the subject say the positive affirmation *once* for each meridian. The one for which he tests weak is the meridian with the problem. For example, you may find someone says, "I am humble," and he tests strong. For "I am happy," he tests strong. But suppose when he says, "I am content," he tests weak. This indicates that he has a basic underlying stomach meridian problem (discontent) to be corrected.

THE MERIDIANS, ASSOCIATED ORGANS, AND NEGATIVE EMOTIONAL STATES

MERIDIAN	ORGANS	NEGATIVE EMOTIONAL STATES
Lung	Lungs	Disdain, Scorn, Contempt, Haughtiness, False Pride, Intolerance, Prejudice
Liver	Liver	Unhappiness
Gall Bladder	Gall Bladder	Rage, Fury, Wrath
Spleen	Spleen Pancreas	Realistic Anxieties about the Future
Kidney	Kidneys Eyes Ears	Sexual Indecision
Large Intestine	Colon Rectum Appendix	Guilt
Circulation-Sex	Adrenals Reproductive Glands	Regret, Remorse, Jealousy, Sexual Tension, Stubbornness
Heart	Heart	Anger
Stomach	Stomach Sinuses	Disgust, Disappointment, Bitterness, Greed, Emptiness, Deprivation, Nausea, Hunger
Thyroid (Triple Heater)	Thyroid Pericardium	Depression, Despair, Hopelessness, Grief, Despondency, Loneliness, Solitude
Small Intestine	Duodenum Small Intestine	Sadness, Sorrow
Bladder	Bladder Urethra	Restlessness, Impatience, Frustration

THE MERIDIANS, ASSOCIATED ORGANS, AND POSITIVE EMOTIONAL STATES

MERIDIAN	ORGANS	POSITIVE EMOTIONAL STATES
Lung	Lungs	Humility, Tolerance, Modesty
Liver	Liver	Happiness, Cheer
Gall Bladder	Gall Bladder	Reaching Out with Love and Forgiveness, Adoration
Spleen	Spleen Pancreas	Faith and Confidence about the Future, Security
Kidney	Kidneys Eyes Ears	Sexual Assuredness
Large Intestine	Colon Rectum Appendix	Self-Worth
Circulation-Sex	Adrenals Reproductive Glands	Renunciation of the Past, Relaxation, Generosity, Abjuration
Heart	Heart	Love, Forgiveness
Stomach	Stomach Sinuses	Contentment, Tranquility
Thyroid (Triple Heater)	Thyroid Pericardium	Hope, Lightness, Buoyancy, Elation
Small Intestine	Duodenum Small Intestine	Joy
Bladder	Bladder Urethra	Peace, Harmony

TEST IMAGES FOR EACH MERIDIAN

Lung	You are with someone who you feel is very silly or ignorant. You feel much smarter and you are very aware of the contrast between your genius and his stupidity, and you feel superior.
Liver	You are very unhappy because your lover has left you. Everything would be perfect if only he would come back to you.
Gall Bladder	Someone has just done something very infuriating. He has just read your most personal letters and your private diary without your permission. You are shouting at him. You want to hit him.
Spleen	Next month's bills are before you. You do not have the money to pay them, and you can see no way of coming up with it.
Kidney	You are having sex with an acquaintance—someone you are not particularly attracted to, yet are not totally turned off by.
Large Intestine	You have just done something over which you feel extremely guilty. Use an example from your own life.
Circulation-Sex	You are in the midst of a long project, and it seems that the project will never be completed. You sincerely regret that you ever began it.
	You are thinking of a person who really turns you on, and the more you think about this person, the more excited you become.

TEST IMAGES FOR EACH MERIDIAN— *Continued*

	You find your lover with a rival and you are trying to figure a way a of getting your lover away from the rival and back for yourself.
Heart	You come back from a walk in the neighborhood and catch a vandal in the act of letting the air out of the tyres of your car.
Stomach	You are walking down the street and see your lover strolling arm-in-arm with someone else. You realize that you have been displaced.
	You have been in line for a promotion for some time. When the vacancy occurs, someone else is given the job.
Thyroid	You are at home, you have no energy, and you have nothing to do worth doing. You feel heavy and weighed down. Everything is just too much!
Small Intestine	You feel full of tears, as if you could cry.
Bladder	You are standing on a bus that is caught in a traffic jam. The bus is moving very, very slowly. You are in a great hurry to get home. You are becoming very upset

Meridian Correlates

Each "bilateral" meridian has a corresponding relationship with a "midline" meridian and vice versa

"Bilateral" Meridians	"Midline" Meridians
Lung	Thyroid
Liver	Stomach
Gall Bladder	Heart
Spleen	Bladder
Kidney	Circulation-Sex
Large Intestine	Small Intestine

The following case history will illustrate how these meridian relationships may be manifested.[41] Bill's wife called me one morning to tell me that a few hours earlier he had been taken to the hospital in an ambulance. He had been having pain around the upper abdomen and chest. He was obviously in great distress. I told her that in view of his history of angina he almost certainly was having a coronary occlusion. She replied, "No, the doctors could find no evidence of a heart attack." They thought there must be something wrong with his abdomen.

They continued to hold this opinion for twenty-four hours—and then evidence of a coronary occlusion was found, or perhaps to put it another way, the evidence of a coronary occlusion developed and was found.

It puzzled me that with Bill's long history of heart pains, the doctors did not immediately find evidence of the coronary occlusion. Why were they so insistent, at least initially, that the problem was not cardiac but abdominal. And afterwards he did have obvious cardiographic signs of a myocardial infarction and was treated accordingly.

Some months later Bill's wife called me again to report that he was having another attack similar to the previous one. I drove over to his home and came to the conclusion that he was not having a coronary attack, for many reasons, not the least of which was the fact that his cardiograph was unchanged, and that his heart meridian was testing strong. When I examined his abdomen I could feel some tensing and guarding of the muscles of the right hypochondrium. As I pushed in more, there was a point of deep and quite painful tenderness. He was having a gall bladder attack! We drove to the cardiologist, who confirmed that, in his opinion, this was not a heart attack. I worked on him physically and relieved the gall bladder tenderness with marked improvement in his general well being.

It now seems quite obvious that Bill was having a gall bladder attack when he was first admitted to the hospital, but that at some point he did also have a coronary occlusion. I am sure that the terrible fear Bill had had for many years that he was going to have a heart attack, as well as the frightening situation in the hospital itself, helped to precipitate it. In a medical text I found the following information: "When the heart is the seat of a proclaimed or a latent disorder, vagal reflexes from a diseased gall bladder may bring about decreased coronary blood flow, arrhythmia or heart-block; the 'cholecystic heart.' " This is what I believe happened to Bill. He was predisposed to a coronary occlusion because of his impaired circulation, which had been a problem for years, but the precipitating factor may have been a result of his diseased gall bladder. The text further stated that "electrocardiographic abnormalities without other evidence of cardiac disease often revert to normal following removal of a diseased gall bladder. Likewise, patients with angina pectoris and pseudo-angina have benefited."[42]

The bilateral meridian that relates to the heart meridian is the gall bladder meridian. There are good psychological reasons why this should be so. The negative emotional attitude associated with the heart meridian is anger and for the gall bladder meridian it is rage. The difference between the two states is that rage is the acting out of the anger. One may feel anger, but one does not just feel rage, one expresses it. In a sense, the gall bladder emotion of rage is a more violent and more primitive attribute of the heart meridian, and the two are intimately related.

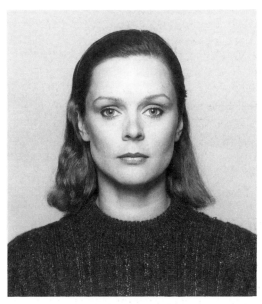

The facial expressions appear to be identical but are subtly different and therefore affect different meridians because the model was thinking different negative thoughts.

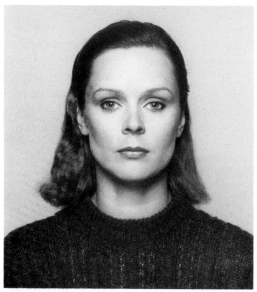

The Deeper Layers

Based upon what you have learned to this point, you now know how to determine your own predominant emotional attitude or that of anyone with whom you come in contact. As you can see, this can be incredibly beneficial in terms of reaching our goal of high life energy, positive health, creativity, and positive emotional balance.

We can now take the technique further and discover the deeper unconscious emotional attitudes that are affecting us. Remember that we are aware only of a small part of our mental functioning.

While the emotional attitudes of which we may well be aware (i.e., those in our pre-conscious), those that we have already tested, are of great importance, they are, as it were, the end results of all the unconscious emotional attitudes that lie beneath them. To get closer to our goal, it is desirable to correct these underlying unconscious layers.

One of the most incredible findings, as you will learn when you do this testing in layers to reveal the unconscious, is that meridians that tested strong will later be revealed as weak after the meridian which is currently testing weak is corrected. Then you correct that meridian and test again, continuing until the thymus tests strong. For example, suppose that at the first level of testing (that is, the level described earlier in this book) you discover that you have a spleen-meridian energy problem. You can test all the other meridians and they will be strong. Now say two or three times with conviction the positive affirmation for the spleen meridian, "I have faith and confidence in my future." As you would expect, the spleen meridian will test strong, but it is now likely that some other meridian that previously tested strong will reveal itself as being weak. It is only after you uncover and correct that first layer of meridian energy imbalance that the second meridian problem reveals itself. There is a definite order in which these layers reveal themselves.

For example, the second layer may have revealed unhappiness (liver meridian). Perhaps you felt that your worries and anxieties about the future were really based on the fact that you wanted someone else to help you, yet this other person had not helped you at all. Your unconscious feeling was, "If only (liver) he would provide me with what I need, then I wouldn't have to worry about being able to pay the rent (spleen)."

To correct the liver-meridian energy imbalance, say with feeling the appropriate affirmation, "I am happy." Another meridian energy imbalance may now reveal itself. It can come to consciousness or pre-consciousness *only* after the layer of unhappiness has been corrected. This may be, for example, a thyroid meridian imbalance. Perhaps underneath you felt depressed, heavy, and hopeless about the whole situation. This is a deeper feeling than the more superficial unhappiness. You correct that with the affirmation, "I am light and buoyant." Now when you test the thymus it is strong, and all meridians also test strong, i.e., spleen→liver→thyroid→thymus.

By implementing this technique you can rapidly reach the unconscious and peel it off in layers, just as occurs in psychotherapy and psychoanalysis.

Isn't it wonderful how these layers reveal themselves? Each emerges only when the more superficial imbalance has been corrected. You continue to go back as in psychotherapy. Every time I have done this, I am amazed that this occurs as it does. It never ceases to thrill me and surprise me. This tool gives us the opportunity to learn many wonderful things about our minds and bodies.

The last, or deepest, meridian imbalance that is corrected prior to the thymus being corrected is the one most affecting it. This type of meridian imbalance frequently tends to be more difficult to correct, and tends to recur. This basic one is, in a sense, the Achilles heel. It is, at least for this period of time (it does change) the deepest, most unconscious psychological factor holding you back. It will often be the lung or thyroid meridian. This occurs because, as I have pointed out, these are the two basic meridians involved in our early development. (The lung meridian relates to Klein's first stage or "position"—that of envy—and the thyroid meridian to her second stage—the depressive position.) Thus ultimately, the lung meridian is the basic meridian involved.

When this is corrected, great changes can occur.

The basic premise here is that you correct the meridian energy imbalance with the affirmation, and then you continually retest and reveal the meridian that is more deeply affected. You do this, like peeling layers off an onion, until you come to the point where the thymus tests strong and continues to test strong. Then you know that both consciously and unconsciously you are balanced and your life energy is really high.

(Very occasionally it will be found that there is more than one meridian testing weak at the same time, but only one of these is the one that "matters"; the other one is what we call static in the system. It is easily abolished or neutralised by taking two or three relaxing breaths. Then we find that this superficial static will disappear and the meridian that remains is the significant one.)

Let me give you an example: A patient of mine—a very attractive career woman in her mid-thirties—was single and having an affair with a married senior executive at the firm for which they both worked. When she first consulted me, she had a liver-meridian energy impairment—she was unhappy. I asked her what she was unhappy about, and she said, "I'm unhappy because my lover is not with me all the time. If only he could be with me all the time, then I would be happy. I know this is what I need for me to be happy, but I also know it is most unlikely to occur because he is too much involved with his wife and family ever to give them up for me." She said the appropriate affirmation with feeling, and her liver meridian tested strong. But her thymus still tested weak. I knew we had more work to do.

Next we discovered a kidney-meridian energy imbalance. I explained to her what this meant—basically, sexual indecision. She agreed. She said, "Yes, that's very true. I was brought up by very strict religious parents and I am concerned about my present sexual relationship with this man. I want to have sex with him; on the other hand I don't know whether I really should, for moral reasons. I also know that perhaps if I do not have sex with him, if I hold out on him, he may be more likely to come around to living with me and giving up his wife. Yes, I definitely am in two minds sexually." Then she said the appropriate affirmation and the kidney meridian tested strong, but her thymus still was testing underactive. We discovered that it was her heart meridian that was imbalanced. I pointed out to her that this meant anger. She suddenly slapped her hand with her fist and said, "Yes. You are right. I am angry with him. I am angry because he has shilly-shallied around with me for years. First he says that he will leave his wife for me, and then he says that he can't. It goes on and on, back and forth. Although I love him very much, I am definitely angry with him." And at this point she became red in the face and her voice grew loud and she said, "You are right—*I am angry!*"

Then she said, "But I can see how it's not really his fault, the poor man is undecided himself. He doesn't know what to do." So I asked her to say, "I love him, I forgive him." Her heart meridian energy imbalance corrected itself. But her thymus was *still* testing underactive. This time we found it was the stomach meridian. After we discussed what that meant, she agreed that she was feeling extremely disappointed. She stated that she felt disappointed every time he left her, that it was as if "he closes the door on me and opens it to his wife. Every time he leaves, I feel disappointed. I have a gnawing pain inside my stomach and I tend to overeat. In fact, in looking back over my life, I would say that disappointment has always been a problem for me. I often feel that I have been let down or that someone else has been chosen and deprived me of my favoured position with a lover. And this is when I go on my eating binges." We re-tested and her thymus tested strong, i.e., liver →kidney→heart→stomach→thymus. The stomach meridian was her Achilles heel.

We had finished our work for this session. Now it was her responsibility to continue to use the appropriate affirmations. I saw her again a few weeks later and she said she felt considerably better and had decided not to see this man anymore. I heard from her a year or so after this; she wrote to me telling me that she was happily married. She told me that she felt that what she had learned about herself in that first session had really enabled her to change her life.

Sometimes it is a good idea to wait and retest in an hour or so, or possibly the next day, after a procedure such as the one outlined above. I remember a patient who went through a similar "unlayering," but in her case, I suggested that she wait for a while in the office.[1] I found on re-testing her an hour later that the thymus, which had tested strong at the end of the session, was now testing weak. That is, there was more work to be done. This is not always required, but such a "mopping up" procedure can be very valuable.

In the case of the latter patient, we found that her small intestine meridian test point was testing weak. I asked, "This whole thing has made you very sad, hasn't it?" She replied that it had. At that point she burst into tears and cried for a long while. When she finished, she thanked me and said that it had been many, many years since she had cried and that she really needed to get it out.

Not long ago, I received an urgent call to see a young man who had suddenly come down with violent abdominal pains. He was gripping the right side of his abdomen and writhing on the floor. He was moaning in pain. He was white. His pulse was racing. He looked like an acute surgical emergency. I was relieved to see that his appendix had already been removed. In fact, the first thing he said to me was, "This is just like when I had my appendix out." He grunted to me between episodes of pain. As I examined him, I became perplexed. I could feel the tension of his abdomen and the spasms of his bowel, but somehow it just didn't "smell" like a surgical case.

I gradually helped him to settle down. His pulse came down to about 90 and he said that the pain was easing off somewhat. Then I tested him and found that the meridian of involvement was the heart meridian. I asked him, "Who are you angry with?" He said, "I'm not angry with anybody." So I asked him to say, "I forgive my father," and he still tested weak at the heart meridian. So it was not his father, nor was it his stepfather. But when he said, "I forgive my mother," the heart meridian tested strong and almost immediately he began to look relieved. He got to his feet. Some colour returned to his cheeks and he said the pain had nearly gone.

I asked him why he was angry with his mother. We discovered that the previous day he had been going through his old school reports, which were far from satisfactory. He was angry because, in his estimation, his mother hadn't done enough to help him at that time. In fact, he felt that she was responsible for the psychological problems that had led to the bad reports and to his having to see numerous psychologists, as well as for his dismissal from a number of schools. It was the anger that had whirled up in him which had precipitated the spasm of the colon. After he transmuted his anger, I tested him further and found a large intestine meridian problem. It was the guilt arising out of his anger toward her that affected him most deeply.

I am not implying that once an unlayering procedure is carried out, there is nothing else to do. I suggest that each day, whenever you can, you have yourself tested to find out what problem you are having at that time so you can instantly correct it before it gets out of hand or develops into a pattern. This way you can keep yourself "up"—full of life energy, not drained by meridian energy imbalances—when reinforced by the daily program.

I had a patient who had experienced a terrible tragedy. His best friend was killed in an accident in which my patient was also involved and from which he is still severely injured. The accident had occurred only a few weeks before. Because my patient was driving the vehicle at the time of the accident, it would be reasonable to expect that the predominant emotions affecting him at the moment would be guilt feeling that perhaps he could have avoided the accident and his friend would still be alive; or possibly grief over the loss of his friend; or perhaps worry about what he was going to do now that he was injured and unable to work. Bringing my psychiatric experience to bear on the case, these were the predominant emotions that I expected to find with him. But as soon as I tested him, I found otherwise. The predominant emotion was anger. Most surprising. When I discussed this with him, however, he readily agreed, and said, "Yes, I am very angry that the accident ever occurred, and I am really angry with the owner of the car. He lent it to me in a condition that predisposed me to the accident."

It was only after the anger was alleviated by the appropriate affirmation that another emotion—depression, grief (thyroid meridian)—revealed itself and could then be confronted and corrected. To have attempted to deal with this emotion (which I suspected at the outset) initially would not have been as effective as dealing with the emotions that were actually present in consciousness and pre-consciousness. At a deep level there was grief, but it had to be dealt with as it arose, as it revealed itself. The way to uncover the grief was to release the anger. This way he was helped far more quickly and thoroughly.

Unconscious Determinants

The art of living is to stay in the present. If my wife does something and I get upset, it should be because what she has done upsets me. But we often find that we carry over patterns of expectation from previous experiences into present ones. We often find, for example, that a husband or wife who has been married previously gets unreasonably upset with what the second spouse has done—not because the current spouse has done something so upsetting, but more because of the memory triggered by the incident. It could and often does even trigger unconscious memories from early childhood and parent-child relationships that were unsatisfactory. To oversimplify, this is what we mean by the *unconscious determinants* of our present activities. So it is important to evaluate any situation in its true present context, rather than invoking past patterns. By peeling off and eradicating those unconscious emotional and meridian energy imbalances that affect us in the present, we can be in a better position to deal with the current situations.

Let me reiterate. One definition of complete psychological normality could be that, regardless of what happened, we would not be extremely negatively affected (stressed) by whatever came along. In other words, our life energy would be high enough that the events that occur in daily life would not interfere with thymus activity and cerebral balance. Of course there is much more to "psychological normality" than that, but for our present purposes it is an adequate description. If we carry out our daily program we should be able to maintain an energy level that allows us to "bounce back" from each little stress to keep all our troops in the armoury prepared for the big battle rather than having them scattered throughout, continually occupied with little skirmishes. A present problem will perhaps affect a meridian only at the superficial testing level and will not trigger a chain of historically emotionally related reactions. In other words, there are no hangups at this time. The achievement of such a state is the major purpose of testing in the various layers and levels—by correcting the unconscious imbalances operant, we are maximising our ability to function harmoniously in the present.

Let us review the general technique of the deeper layer testing and correction.

1. As previously, test the thymus. If it is underactive, then test the hemispheres. If the person is left-hemisphere dominant, test the "midline" meridian test points; and if he is right hemi-phered dominant, test the "bilateral" meridian test points.
2. Find the meridian that is underactive. Have the person repeat the appropriate positive affirmation. On re-testing you will find that the meridian tests strong now.

3.   Repeat the thymus test. If it is strong, you need go no further. You are probably working with a relatively emotionally healthy person capable of living in and working in the present. If the thymus tests weak, repeat the hemispheres test. Find the involved meridian, correct it with the affirmation, and retest the thymus. If it is testing strong, you have finished. If it still tests weak, then repeat the hemispheres and meridian tests and correct what you find. It is generally only necessary to repeat this procedure two or three times until you have found the Achilles heel and corrected it.

A man came to see me and he was obviously very tense. His voice was tense, he gripped his hands tightly together, and when I touched his body to test him I could feel the tension within him. He complained primarily of back pains and chronic constipation. On testing I found, as expected, that his thymus was underactive. I tested each hemisphere and discovered that he was left-hemisphere dominant at this time, so I then tested the meridians with midline test points. I found that it was the circulation-sex meridian that was de-vitalised. I was not surprised, knowing that this meridian is often involved in cases of tension such as this.

I had three major categories of emotions to discuss with him relative to this meridian involvement. I suggested that, in view of his overall picture, it was probably the aspect of tension that was most affecting him. With this he agreed and said, "Yes, I am very tense, and I even know deep down that if I could only relax, this back problem would go away." We then discussed the possibility that his tension might have a sexual problem at its source. He was in his mid-fifties. He said that he had never been married, never had a serious affair, and actually had had only a few sexual experiences in his life. He had no close female friends. He had been troubled by persistent sexual thoughts and he was constantly trying, usually unsuccessfully, to push them out of his mind. I suggested that he repeat the affirmation, "I am relaxed," and that he visualise himself in a very relaxed state. On re-testing the circulation-sex meridian, we found that the imbalance had corrected itself. But his thymus was still testing weak. Even so, he suddenly said, "My back feels easier than it has in years!" On palpating the involved area, I did find that the muscle tension had relaxed somewhat.

We re-tested his hemispheres and found a right-hemisphere dominance. On testing the "bilateral" meridians we found that the large intestine meridian (guilt) was affected. Remember, this meridian had not tested weak in the first procedure. It had revealed an imbalance only after the sexual tension problem had been recognised and corrected. I asked him if perhaps he felt guilty over sex in general or over a specific sexual incident, to which he replied, "No, not really." However, you will recall that the deeper layers of imbalance are generally unconscious, that is, not within the subject's conscious knowledge. After he considered this possibility, he then said, "You know, that's a very reasonable question. I am a strict Catholic and I know that it is wrong to masturbate, and wrong to have sexual intercourse before marriage. So every time I consider one of these activities, suddenly I am overwhelmed with guilt. Yes, I can see that this is what has been happening to me over the years."

He then repeated the affirmation for the large intestine meridian, "I am basically clean and good. I am worthy of being loved." He had a look of amazement on his face when we tested and found that now his large intestine meridian test point was strong. He said, "Well, you have helped me to face something about myself that I had kept hidden all these years. That is really amazing."

On testing his thymus again we found that there was more work to be done. He was still right-hemisphere dominant, and on testing we found the lung meridian was now involved. With the correction and release of energy in the large intestine and circulation-sex meridians, his body was now able to express its "problems" with the lung meridian. Now, as you might have discovered for yourself by this time, it is often difficult to discuss the emotional attitudes associated with lung-meridian energy imbalances with a person without appearing to insult him.

I began carefully to outline what the emotional concomitants of the lung meridian were, and this man was quite surprised at what was revealed. Now in psychiatry every patient is different, but after twenty or more years of practice, one soon assesses a situation and knows where the problem areas are. So I suggested to this man that although his appearance was one of meekness and humility there was a fair amount of superiority operating—and I suggested that perhaps because of his sexual aloofness he had developed this feeling. He thought about this and agreed. When he said, "I am humble" with a clear understanding of the true meaning of the word, he tested strong. He said that he found little difficulty in accepting these findings after considering them. "After all," he said, "my own body is telling me these things." Now his thymus tested strong, and he left knowing what work he had to do.

When I saw him several weeks later, he was a changed man. He came in smiling; he seemed much more at ease with himself in general. He was far less tense and he reported that his back had given him minimal problems. The most remarkable thing for him, he said, was the change in his bowels. He had been constipated for many years, normally having a bowel action only every three days or so. Since that first session, he was having regular bowel actions once and sometimes twice each day without laxatives. He was very pleased that he now understood himself better, and said that he realised why he had such difficulty in finding someone to whom he would like to be married. But he was confident that with continued work he would soon attract the type of person with whom he could easily establish a long-term relationship. He re-emphasised that the most important thing for him was that he understood himself better. He saw very clearly the interdependence of the functions of his body, mind, and spirit and now he was able to work toward the development and achievement of his goal.

Let's take another example. I once had to make a decision as to which of two assistants to hire on a full-time basis. They were both students and part-time assistants and were both very helpful. After I had made the decision and one assistant had started her full-time job, the other one came to me and asked that we test her, as she felt that something just wasn't right. She had been a student long enough to be aware when something was out of balance. Her thymus tested weak and we found left-hemisphere dominance. On testing the "midline" meridians, we found the stomach meridian was involved. She was already familiar with this work, and she exclaimed, "Well, obviously I'm disappointed! I am very upset that you chose the other student for the job. I feel that I deserved that job, and I do feel literally *dis*appointed. I feel that I had developed a relationship with you that has now been broken in some way. You have transferred your trust to someone else." We then took some time to discuss my reasons for employing the other student and I reassured her that our relationship, from my standpoint, was as good as ever. I expected to find then that her thymus tested strong, and that would be the end of the discussion. Instead, though, we found her thymus weak and her left hemisphere was still dominant. On testing, a circulation-sex meridian problem was revealed. She said, "I know why. It's because I'm jealous. I feel that the appointment was *mine* and that the other student has taken it away from me." She thought for a moment and said, with great insight, "You know, this is identical to the situation I have always had at home. I'm the younger sister and I have always felt that my older sister is given preferential treatment, that she is given things and attention that are rightfully mine." She repeated the appropriate affirmation with conviction, and we found that her thymus was strong.

She has remained a student and part-time assistant for some time now, and she has maintained a good relationship with the rest of my staff, including her "rival." She had recognised and corrected her disappointment first and then her jealousy. As a side benefit, she recently reported that since our discussion her relationship with her sister has been remarkably better and that she feels much more comfortable in her family in general.

In view of what you have just read, you may begin to wonder how significant a first-layer meridian imbalance is in developing a long-term program for yourself. It depends on how often that meridian imbalance is operant. If it was only of short duration, then it should not be a cause for concern. But if you are experiencing physical symptoms such as a headache or upset stomach or the like and you find a meridian imbalance, then it is significant. By relieving the emotional concomitant you will help to relieve the physical symptoms (I am not implying that you will cure it). On the other hand, if you consistently find one meridian testing weak, that indicates an area for work. Long-term imbalances in the meridian will ultimately affect the organ it serves. So by correcting the imbalances at an emotional level, at an energy level, we are practicing prevention. We may be able to prevent a physical problem from developing.

In most cases where there is meridian energy imbalance, laboratory tests show no evidence of abnormality. It is often too early for that. And this is a wonderful aspect of our research. It often allows us to practice primary prevention.

Another point to be considered in assessing the value or importance of a first-layer meridian imbalance is that what you find on testing indicates the predominant emotional state operant at that time. You can learn what is holding you back right now. You can then correct it and release the energy that is blocked in that meridian and get yourself back in order. You are in a better position to achieve your full potential, to function with maximum life energy.

The Double-Bind

Soon after I first obtained my driver's license, I was driving alone when I came to an intersection controlled by a traffic policeman. He looked straight at me and put his hand up in a "stop" gesture and said in a loud commanding voice, "Come on!" Immediately I felt tremendously anxious. I didn't know what to do. Did he mean for me to come on, or did he mean for me to stop? What was I to do? Whatever I did would be wrong. If I went with his verbal command, I would be disobeying his gesture. If I went with his gesture, I would be disobeying his verbal command. All I could see was disaster, whatever I did. If I went forward, I was wrong; if I didn't go forward, I was wrong. My panic increased. Worst of all, I had no one to turn to for advice.

This is what we mean by the double-bind. This phrase was coined by Gregory Bateson, who felt that this communication process was one of the most important factors in the causation of schizophrenia.[1] One of the models that the advocates of this theory proposed was that the mother had mixed feelings toward the child and when she would, for example, ask the child to come close because she loved him, as he got closer, she would start to push him away. Her own heightened mixed feelings became intolerable as he approached. The child given this conflicting message does not know what to do. He wonders, "Do I go with what she says, or do I go with what I feel she is saying with her gestures?" The important aspect of the double-bind is that there is a *contradictory communication being given simultaneously using two different modalities.* It is not saying to someone, "I love you," and then following this with, "I hate you," because that is not simultaneous and it is the same modality of communication. But when you say, "I love you" but the expression on your face is one of anger, this is a double-bind. The transmitter of the message is in two minds. Does the mother basically like or dislike the child? Her own confusion is transmitted to the child, and now he becomes confused.

The other important ingredient in the model is that there is no external authority to whom to turn and ask, for example, "What did Mummy mean? Did she mean 'I love you,' or did she mean, 'I hate you'?" Just as I had no one in the car to ask, the child has no one to use as a point of reality reference. Further, the model has the strong, dominant, double-binding mother along with a very weak father. The father says, in essence, "I have enough problems with your mother myself. I don't understand her either. Don't come to me with your problems about her." This is the basic conceptual model for the factors leading to the double-bind.

A psychiatrist or anyone listening to people discussing their problems begins to realise that this situation is not reserved for schizophrenics or even for psychotics. It is occurring to each of us every day. What of the government that declares it believes 100 percent in peace yet engages in provocative acts, for example? Or what of the agency that is established solely for the purpose of implementing energy conservation programs but which daily condones activities that mitigate against it? A company may advertise that its sole purpose for existence is to serve the good of the people—while it reports windfall profits. Or what of the advertisements that indicate the appeal of smoking while quoting the surgeon general's warning on the ad? Or the pretty, coquettish girl who leads the boy on and then says, "Whatever gave you the idea that I would want to have sex with you?" Her body is saying yes, her voice is saying no. What is he to believe?

Think of the double-binds a politician may be capable of giving when he makes statements such as, "I think that the free enterprise system is absolutely too important to be left to the voluntary action of the marketplace." (*Environmental Action*, December, 1979)

Consider the stereotyped situation. The husband comes home from work and can sense by the way his wife is walking around the house that something is not right. He hears her heavy, aggressive footsteps, hard on her heels. She is clattering the cooking ware, saying little, and has a disturbed expression on her face. He says to her, "What's wrong, honey?" and her standard reply is, "Nothing." Now what is he to believe? He can *sense* from her every gesture and "vibration" that she is upset, but she *says* nothing is wrong. He is now caught in a double-bind situation.

And what of the husband who comes in at 3 A.M., exhausted after an obviously heavy night. His wife asks, "What have you been doing?" and he replies, "Nothing." These are all double-bind situations. They destroy our life energy; they will drive us crazy, perhaps not psychotic, but certainly in the loose sense of the word, crazy.

To test your response to a double-bind, use a sample situation such as the one described at the beginning of this chapter. Have someone test you in the clear. You should test strong. Now have a third person say to you while looking at you, "Come here." You should again test strong. Then have the third person remain silent but put up his hand in a "stop" gesture. You should again test strong. But now, have your partner test you while you are experiencing both messages simultaneously. The third person says, "Come here," while at the same time he has his hand up in the "stop" gesture. Now you will find that, if you are like 90 percent of individuals, your life energy has been depleted by this stress and you will test weak. You, like most of us, are vulnerable to this double-bind. Of course, if your life energy were higher, you would not be vulnerable, and it is my hope that what you learn from this book will give you this capacity.

The next question that arises is, which of the two messages in this communication are you believing? How do you respond to this ambiguous, simultaneous love/hate message? First, test to see whether under this type of stress you tend to become left- or right-hemisphere dominant. To determine this, simply test for hemisphere dominance as you are being given the double-bind message. If your response is left-hemisphere dominance, it means that you are basically accepting the "good" part of the communication. You realise that the message is a mixed one, and you choose to ignore the "stop" and accept the "come here." Conversely, if your response is right-hemisphere dominance, then you again recognise the contradictory nature of the message, but you respond to the "stop" portion.

I have tested many patients and students using this system, and I have found that those who test left-hemisphere dominant in response to the stress of the double-bind communication tend to be able not to be upset by a form of rejection. These people will try again, recognising that the communication is mixed and hoping that the next time the response will be positive. They are basically optimistic. Those individuals whose response to the stress of the double-bind transmission is to become right-hemisphere dominant are more likely to be put off by the rejection and not try again. They tend to be more pessimistic.

Note: You may test right- or left-hemisphere dominant in a situation that is double binding, but for it to be a true double-bind, the specific meridian involved must be the primary one for each hemisphere. Lung is the basic meridian for the right hemisphere, and thyroid for the left hemisphere. This is in keeping with Klein's first position (paranoid-schizoid) and second position (depressive).

Listen to what your friends, your relatives, advertisements, government reports, tell you. You may begin to realise how we are affected by all communications, and how binding communications tend to lower life energy. After all, it takes a great deal of energy just to interpret the message and to determine what portions you will believe. But recognise that if you can activate your life energy sufficiently, you will not be affected. In this world of increasing "binds," this can be a comforting and reassuring thought.

THE DOUBLE-BIND
The model's contradictory message will cause you to test weak unless your life energy
is high. Are you able to overcome it? If not, which hemisphere becomes dominant?
   The eyes say "yes," the hand says "no."
   The eyes say "come," the hand says "go."

The Daily Program for Life Energy

You have learned how you can correct the negative emotional attitudes that are affecting your life energy as a result of stresses to which you have been subjected. You can correct these whether they be caused by past or recent experiences, whether they be conscious or unconscious.

In order for you to enjoy a more healthy, harmonious life, I suggest a simply daily meditational program to activate and vitalise your meridians. It is not necessary to test for individual meridian imbalances—and this is of particular benefit if you do not have a test partner.

Use this program several times each day routinely, and especially when stressed. This is a way of practicing true prevention—abolishing problems at an energy level before they have a chance to develop physically.

If possible, this program is best carried out if you adopt the Alexander horizontal position,[1] a position for general postural improvement. It is taught as part of the Alexander Technique that was developed by F. Matthias Alexander, and it can be extremely beneficial. It aligns the body, thereby permitting a free flow of energy throughout and enabling the thymus to monitor and correct imbalances. The position is as follows: Lie down with your knees bent, your feet flat on the floor, and the outside of your thighs parallel to your hips. Put a book or two under your head so that your spine and neck are aligned. In this position you will be relaxed and receptive to energising influences. And in this position, your body is in balance and your body energies are balanced; you are in an optimum situation to benefit from your meditational experience. Put the tip of your tongue on the rugae, and breathe in and out through your nose until you begin to feel relaxed.[2]

Now go through each meridian in turn, saying with conviction the positive affirmations for each. It is helpful, although not essential, to touch the test point(s) for the particular meridian at the time you say the affirmation. Say them in any order you find comfortable, finishing with the affirmations for the thymus. Say them either aloud or to yourself, and at the same time visualise the associated positive feelings.[3] Allow your breath to flow on its own. Say each affirmation three times, with three successive breaths, and continue until you end with the thymus affirmation. As you do the final affirmations you may wish to tap your thymus area for reinforcement. Think of your energy being balanced and flowing smoothly and lovingly into all your organs. Imagine them all working in complete harmony for the total enrichment of your health and well-being. Close with the affirmation: "My life energy is high. I am in the state of love."

This is a very simple meditational program. I have taught it to hundreds of students over the years. Many have said that, just as a final positive reinforcement, they like to concentrate on their homing thought before ending the meditation. This simple procedure can be very rewarding, and it can assist you in achieving your goal.

DAILY AFFIRMATION PROGRAM

I have love,
    faith,
    trust,
    gratitude,
  and courage.
	Thymus

I am humble.	
I am tolerant.	
I am modest.	Lung
I am happy.	
I have good fortune.	
I am cheerful.	Liver
I reach out with love.	Gall Bladder
I am secure.	Spleen

142

My sexual energies are balanced.	Kidney
I am basically clean and good.	
I am worthy of being loved.	Large Intestine
I renounce the past.	
I am generous.	
I am relaxed.	Circulation-Sex
I have forgiveness in my heart.	Heart
I am content.	
I am tranquil.	Stomach
I am buoyed up with hope.	
I am light and buoyant.	Thyroid
I am jumping with joy.	Small Intestine
I am in harmony.	
I am at peace.	Bladder
I have love,	

faith,

trust,

gratitude,

and courage.   Thymus

close with:

My life energy is high.

I am in the state of love.

We have found that the therapeutic power of the positive affirmation can be increased if it is said in an impersonal way. For example, if instead of saying, "I am content," Bill says, "Bill is content," there will be, on deeper levels of testing, a greater increase in energy. The reason for the heightened effect of the impersonal positive affirmation is that it involves the act of thinking, of putting out a message into the world which then comes back to you. Whenever we direct our communication out into the world, whether it be speech, writing, poetry, music, or the like, there will always be a greater increase in life energy than if we keep the message to ourselves. In this context, it is very important to listen intently to the words as they come back to you and focus on taking them in.

Overcoming Fears and Phobias

All of us are troubled in particular circumstances by apprehensions and fears concerning a future event. It is now possible to discover and easily correct these with the knowledge that you have already acquired. Consider the following examples: A woman told me that she knew she wanted to get married but she also knew there was something holding her back, always preventing it. She found it difficult even to talk about it. I asked her to think about being married—exactly what she thought about I do not know, but it was what marriage meant to her. On testing her, we found that the small intestine meridian was weak. When we discussed the emotions related to this meridian, she said, "Yes, that's appropriate. I think what I fear about marriage is that it is going to make me sad and tearful. I'm afraid I will end up crying throughout my marriage as my mother seemed to do throughout hers."

A student recently told me that she was very frightened about going to the dentist for her appointment the next day. She said that in fact whenever she goes to the dentist she is in a state of extreme distress. She asked if I could help. I asked her to think of being in a dentist's chair. We found that her thymus tested weak. As we continued testing we found that in her case the particular meridian involved was the stomach meridian. We were unable to find a conscious reason why this meridian should be involved, so I suggested to her that she continue repeating the associated affirmation, "I am content," reinforcing it with the thymus thump. I suggested that she do this as often as she could before she saw the dentist and then while she was being treated by him. Both she and the dentist later told me how much better that session had been than any of her previous ones. She reported that she felt very little fear and apprehension and the dentist told me that for the first time he could really do proper work on her as she was no longer so tense and fearful.

We have been able to reduce stress and anxiety with many students about to undergo any form of operative procedure, dental or surgical, with gratifying results.

Whenever you are approaching a fearful situation, such as going to the dentist, perhaps taking a trip on an airplane, being interviewed for a new job, sitting for an examination, attending court, or whatever, visualise the situation strongly in your mind and then test to find the impaired meridian. Work on keeping that meridian as activated as possible prior to and during the stressful experience. You could be quite surprised at the help this will give you.

In the same manner you can help yourself to overcome, for example, the smoking habit. Think of smoking and you will find that your thymus will test weak. A specific meridian, usually the lung meridian, will also test weak. You will find that you can help yourself to stop smoking by concentrating on the lung affirmation to ease the withdrawal.

At times when you think of highly stressful situations, and smoking is one, you will find that you will be so weakened that your indicator muscle will test weak. Just thinking of it, without test-touching the thymus, is stressful enough to cause the muscle to test weak. In such cases, you will find that test-touching one and only one meridian will cause the muscle to stay strong when you think of the highly stressful situation. This is what we call double-negative testing. The meridian that causes the muscle that is weak in the clear to test strong is the involved meridian. This double testing applies when the stressful situation is so great that it diminishes your life energy and causes the indicator muscle to test weak even before the thymus test-touching procedure is carried out.

This method can also be beneficial in terms of goal direction. Another friend told me that he had always wished he could strike it rich with one of his wildcat oil-drilling schemes. So I asked him to think of striking it rich. We found that this thought weakened his liver meridian, strange as this may seem. When we asked him to think not just of striking it rich with oil, but also of using that money for philanthropic purposes (which he really wants to do, and which would be more important to him than any personal material wealth), he tested strong. He thanked me and said, "Well, I realise my goal is not to get money through oil. My goal is to do something for other people when I have the money, which I hope to get through the oil." Thus he has the beginning of his homing thought.

A patient told me that she had great difficulty swallowing. As soon as she put something solid in her mouth to swallow—like a pill—she would become extremely apprehensive and fearful and would choke. Because of this, she was unable to take vitamins and food supplements, which she truly needed for her health, and was on a soft diet for many years.

I asked her to think of swallowing a pill. Immediately, her circulation-sex meridian test point was weak. As soon as she said the appropriate affirmation and kept it clearly in her mind, she was able to swallow with ease. Since then, she has had very little difficulty with her swallowing, and whenever she does have problems, she just reinforces the affirmations with the thymus thump, and her problem is once again resolved.

Elena was born in Hungary, and she lived there until a tragedy occurred when she was fourteen years old. Within a short period of time, right at the end of World War II, her father and mother were imprisoned (as she was herself for a brief period of time), tortured, and beaten. For three months after Elena's release from prison, she was anxiously searching for her father (who was, in fact, dead), and desperately trying to get her mother out of prison. Her mother eventually was released, but within two weeks of that both of Elena's maternal grandparents died in front of her.

Since that time, she has had terrible memories, nightmares, and thoughts of her Hungarian experience. That period affects her so much that whenever she thinks anything in her native Hungarian language, let alone says it aloud, she becomes extremely stressed and apprehensive.

What could we do about this? First, we had to find out which meridian was predominantly affected when she thought of her Hungarian experience. We found that Elena's gall bladder meridian was affected—that she was feeling rage. So she said and incorporated with deep feeling the affirmation as part of her daily program. Soon she was able to talk more freely about the experiences, and she overcame most, but not all, of her apprehension and stress when speaking or hearing her native language.

A student told me that he had a fear of heights that was extremely debilitating and distressing to him, and it greatly interfered with his functioning. He was a sane, rational man, a scientist, very logically oriented. Tranquillisers and psychotherapy had failed to relieve him of his fear. When he consulted me, I asked him to think of being on top of a very tall building. Instantly his thymus tested weak. We found that the specific meridian involved was the circulation-sex meridian. (With true phobias it is almost invariably this meridian which is involved.) I then showed him, to his own amazement, that if while thinking of this phobic situation he also said to himself with conviction the affirmation, "I am relaxed," he no longer tested weak. I pointed out to him that now he could see just how powerful positive thoughts could be in helping him to overcome his phobic situation. "Well," he said with a smile, "I'll think about it." It was obvious that he was not at all confident that such a simple technique could be of any benefit.

When I next saw him, he came into my office with a huge smile on his face. He shook my hand warmly and said, "You won't believe what happened. My wife bought tickets to the opera for us. When we arrived there, I discovered that our seats were in one of the back rows right at the top of the theatre. I immediately became very stressed and apprehensive and thought, 'I can't possibly sit there. It will kill me!' But I decided to try what you said. While walking up the stairs I said the affirmations. To my amazement I was able to sit through and enjoy the total performance. You've got a believer."

Most of us have had fears and phobias at some point in our lives. Many people become extremely frightened when they are about to have an injection or have blood drawn. Some people refuse to get into an elevator or to go into a room with no windows. Others are afraid of developing a specific dreaded disease. Whatever the fear, it drains life energy. Now we have a way to take care of such energy drains. With the energy that is gained, we are free to pursue our goal of positive health.

Transmutation

"To become renewed, transfigured, in another pattern." — T. S. Eliot

Modern psychiatry often reinforces our feelings of helplessness and dependency by neglecting the role of the patient's will. Of course we all know there are many people who seem to want to stay in the negative, but this may be because they don't realise that they are in the negative—that there can be a "positive!" I believe that if they did, they would make the change.

One of the problems with psychiatry is that we have become obsessed with finding out *why* we are upset. The important point is not what has made us upset, but in which way we are upset and how we can overcome it, and how to raise the vitality, the life energy. The *why* has to do with left-brain investigation, but the true change within the individual comes when both brains and the thymus are involved in the decision. And it comes from discovering the exact emotional state involved, as you can do with the techniques described in this book, and then working to transmute, to turn that emotional state into the specific positive. So it is not a question of *why*. It is a question of identifying the state and then activating our life energy, our wills to be well, to turn it into the positive. This is the dual-hemisphere, creative approach to the problem.

By transmutation I mean the ability instantly to turn the negative into the positive. As an example, let us say that you are tested by a friend and it is found that your liver meridian is weak. Your first step toward turning this into the positive is to recognise that you are unhappy. Then choose to give up the unhappiness and take on the positive feeling of being happy and blissful. Just say the appropriate affirmation with conviction, and visualise it strongly and clearly, and the negative becomes positive. This is transmutation.

To want to do this, and to want to continue to do it, your will to be well must be present. This is your active contribution to your health, to your life, to attaining your goal. You must want to be well, and then you can easily go about achieving it.

Let's be very clear as to what is meant by transmutation. If you are angry, for example, I am not recommending that you push your anger down inside you. That only hurts you in other ways. Nor am I suggesting that you act out the anger. That hurts both you and the other person. What I am suggesting is that you transmute it. Recognise that you have the anger, recognise that it is hurting you and others, and then say the appropriate positive affirmation with conviction. You will then activate your will to be well and you will overcome the anger with positive emotions. Your anger no longer exists. It has been transformed, transmuted, into something positive and productive, and your life energy has been stimulated.

All this has important implications for psychosomatic medicine. We know, on the one hand, that negative emotional states ultimately lead to physical illness—heart disease, cancer, diabetes, asthma, and so on. But we also now know precisely which emotional attitudes may lead to precisely which diseases, because we know the emotional states that are related to each meridian, and therefore each organ that becomes diseased.

Thus, you can see how psychosomatic illness begins. The mental attitudes and emotional states interfere with the energy supply through the meridian, and to the specific organ. That is how the mind affects the body. In most psychosomatic conditions, there is an "interaction between psychological factors and a physiological predisposition to the illness." [1] You can also see that if we correct the emotional attitudes, if we continually buoy ourselves up by transmuting negative into positive, we can keep our energy balanced and practice primary prevention.

What happens if an individual already has a disease? We know that there are physical diseases that feed back and cause emotional problems. These are called somato-psychic diseases. Again, we know what specific emotional problems will tend to be caused by or to accompany the various physical diseases.

Thus, even if we do not subscribe to the belief that the emotional state causes the illness, at least when people have illness we can then identify the accompanying emotional states. Even if it is too late for an individual to correct his emotional imbalances and prevent the occurrence of disease, at least the emotional component can be stopped from feeding back into the disease. This can be done with the use of the appropriate positive affirmations, among many other things.

In these chapters I have outlined a new approach to preventive and psychosomatic medicine, as well as to psychiatry. But more importantly, I believe it is a major breakthrough for *you.* You, as an educated layman, can now carry out important research into psychosomatic medicine. You do not require a laboratory, and you do not need multi-million-dollar grants. All you need is some people to test, some inquiring minds, and the facts presented here. You can do some very important work just by testing yourself and your friends and seeing time and again the relationship between specific emotional states and organs.

It is incredible to think that each organ has a specific corresponding emotional state, but this is our finding. We can now begin to understand certain personality types—the asthmatic and the lung meridian, the diabetic and the spleen meridian, and so forth—and to open up tremendous vistas.

It is my hope that in some way you have learned how to be well—and how to identify the specific problems and attitudes that were holding you back. Now you can easily, positively, and simply work to turn them around, to transmute the negative into positive states of love, faith, gratitude, trust, and courage. This is the reason I have written this book.

Our goal is to function as much like an adult as possible in life, free of encumbrances of past problems and stresses. This we can accomplish by peeling back the layers and then correcting specific emotional problems that are affecting us. When these are corrected, we will be invulnerable to most stress and our energies will be released to be devoted to our true purpose in life. Our *thymos* will be active and our energies will no longer be dissipated fighting stressful battles throughout the body and mind. We can begin to discover our deepest homing thoughts, our true selves, and to mobilise our energies to achieve our positive goals. Our life energy will be free and detached from the negative and will be moving into the sunshine, into positive health. While I do not believe that this book alone will make possible the full achievement of our potentials (would that that were the case!), I do hope and believe that it will be a beneficial tool in achieving development and maturation.

As I stated at the beginning of this book, in my years in psychiatry and preventive medicine I was often very disappointed and unhappy to see myself and my peers falling so short of our potentials, not going where our endowments and heritages could lead. Now I know that if you carry out the procedures that we have discussed, much less of your life energy will be drained in trying to cope with negative attitudes and debilitating stresses. You will be liberated, your own master. You will know your purpose in life and can set about achieving it. I hope and pray that you reach your goal, your home.

"Love is the lesson which the Lord us taught." (Edmund Spenser)

Epilogue

My hope is that now you have an understanding of the supreme importance of your life energy for your mental and physical health. You also now know about the function of each of the hemispheres of your brain, and you have learned that the balanced activity of both hemispheres is required for problem-solving and creativity. You have learned how to correct any imbalance so that you are now able to be one of that 5 percent or so of the population that is truly creative. You can now find new solutions, the proper solutions, to the problems of life. You can use your whole brain to help yourself and everyone around you. You now have the equipment and the knowledge to understand yourself as has never before been possible.

You have also learned about each of the emotional states and how each is related through the specific acupuncture meridian to particular organs of the body. This is the basis of the mind-body link and the foundation of a holistic understanding of our total functioning, mental and physical. You have learned how you can assist your life energy to help overcome any physical problem you may have by invoking the power of your thoughts to correct the accompanying specific negative emotional state. And more importantly, you have learned how every physical illness starts with a particular negative emotion. Thus by frequently monitoring ourselves and correcting these early negative states, the precursors of physical disease, we can keep ourselves healthy. We can practice the positive prevention of disease.

You have learned a simple technique of affirmations that may be carried out on a daily basis and also whenever you are stressed.

This simple technique will help to keep you emotionally balanced, with all your emotions in the positive. Thus your life energy will be high and you will be healthy. Now all your emotions can be positive and the life energy that courses throughout your body and your soul can be uplifted with love. This is what I mean by psycho-biological harmony. And through these simple procedures, it is yours.

I hope as well that you have now learned a love for your language and a respect for the myriad psychological insights within it, especially the power of the word. I hope you feel humble and awed in the presence of what you have learned about the incredible richness and subtlety of our mental and physical functioning.

You have learned how to find out what is really going on inside you, what you really feel and believe and desire, by the application of a simple technique. You have learned the wonderful world of mental and physical functioning that is now at your fingertips for investigation as a result of this simple test. You now have a most powerful research tool to use on yourself and your friends. Now you can learn what is really right for you—not just what you *think* is right—in all aspects of your functioning. Now and only now can you make the right choices for your life. You can elicit information from your deepest unconscious and find out what you really feel and what you are really thinking, and what you really want in life. This can be of incredible benefit to you. Used with care it will change your life. You will be able as never before to develop and unfold and to achieve your own personal evolution.

I could have written a more scientifically rigorous book, one which might possibly have won acclaim from my professional colleagues. But that would have been another left-brain book. As my purpose has been to help you change your life, it is important that I address your right brain as well. Your left brain is already so overwhelmed by your day-to-day living that it is deaf to the new message. It cannot hear anymore, and if it cannot hear it cannot be helped. Hence I have written this book to talk to your right brain as well as to your left. I want to help you to understand, to "see," and thus to grow and to learn—to learn who you were created to be and then to grow into your true self—by at all times keeping your eye on your homing thought, your true goal in life.

You have learned the supreme power of your thoughts. Over the centuries philosophers and psychologists have speculated on this, but now you have been able to experience something previously undemonstrable: the immediate power of your thoughts to influence your physical state. Your thoughts have the power to alter the physiological response of your muscles. A thought or a word can change the energy of the organ. This you can prove for yourself. Thoughts have the power to cause or cure illness in your body. You can now use them for health.

What I hope more than anything else is that from reading this book you have learned the supreme power of love and can now demonstrate it. It is love that banishes all the negative emotions. It is love that invokes the spirit and activates the life energy. It is love that balances our brains and makes us creative. And it is love for our true self, for the self that we can be, that drives us on to want to be better and want to be healthier and to want to be more evolved. Love is health and life.

Appendix I

MAJOR ETYMOLOGICAL REFERENCES

Some of these books have been my friends for many years. I have grown to love them, as they have given me many hours of quiet satisfaction. I hope that this work may stimulate you to explore these monuments of our society and to treasure and value them as they deserve. To know our language is to know ourselves, and to love our language is to love ourselves.

Perhaps the best place to start is with Partridge's *Origins* and the *American Heritage Dictionary*. Most importantly, please do not be overwhelmed by the size of the *Oxford English Dictionary*. To me, it is the greatest inexhaustible treasure house.

American Heritage Dictionary of the English Language. New York: American Heritage Publishing Company, 1969.

Benveniste, Emil. *Indo-European Language and Society.* London: Faber and Faber, 1973.

Buck, Carl D. *A Dictionary of Selected Synonyms in the Principal Indo-European Languages.* Chicago: University of Chicago Press, 1949.

Crabbe, George. *English Synonyms.* New York: Harper Brothers, 1890.

Johnson, Samuel. *A Dictionary of the English Language.* New York: AMS Press, 1967. (reprint)

Klein, Ernest. *A Comprehensive Etymological Dictionary of the English Language.* Amsterdam: Elsevier, 1967.

Lewis, Charlton T., and Short, Charles. *A Latin Dictionary.* Oxford: Clarendon Press, 1879. 1969.

MacDonald, A. M. *Etymological English Dictionary*. Paterson, N.J.: Littlefield, Adams, 1964.

McDonell, Arthur A. *A Practical Sanskrit Dictionary*. Oxford: Oxford University Press, 1958.

Morris, William, and Morris, Mary. *Morris Dictionary of Word and Phrase Origins*. New York: Harper and Row, 1977.

Onions, C. T. *The Oxford Dictionary of English Etymology*. Oxford: Clarendon Press, 1966.

Oxford English Dictionary. Oxford: Clarendon Press, 1933, 1961.

Partridge, Eric. *Origins—A Short Etymological Dictionary of Modern English*. 4th ed. London: Routledge and Kegan Paul, 1966.

Pokorny, Julius. *Indogermanisches Etymologisches Worterbuch*. Bern: Francke, 1959.

Shipley, Joseph T. *Dictionary of Word Origins*. New York: Philosophical Library, 1945.

Skeat, Walter W. *An Etymological Dictionary of the English Language*. 4th ed. Oxford: Clarendon Press, 1910.

——— . *Principles of English Etymology*. Oxford, 1887.

Smith, Charles John. *Synonyms Discriminated*. London: George Bell and Sons, 1910.

Webster's New International Dictionary. 2nd ed. Springfield, Mass.: G. & C. Merriam, 1944.

Weekley, Ernest. *An Etymological Dictionary of Modern English*. New York: Dover, 1967.

Wyld, Henry C. *The Universal Dictionary of the English Language*. London: Routledge and Kegan Paul, 1961.

For further information on the work of Dr. John Diamond and The Institutes for the Enhancement of Life Energy and Creativity, please write to:

The Diamond Center
P.O. Box 381
South Salem, NY 10590
USA

Appendix II

NOTES
INTRODUCTION

1. Plato wrote in *Symposium* (186D), "[The doctor] ought to be able to bring about love and reconciliation between the most antithetic elements in the body... Our ancestor Asclepius knew how to bring love and concord to these opposites, and he it was, as poets say and I believe, who founded our art."

2. *Fragments Of Empedocles*, trans. William E. Leonard, (LaSalle, III., 1973).

3. Wright, M. R. ed. *Empedocles: The Extant Fragments*. (New Haven: Yale University Press), 1981, pp. 30-34.

4. Of course, the concept of the interaction of the mind and the body is not new. Consider the definition of *emotion* as "a strong excitement of feeling, tending to manifest itself by its effect upon the body." Charles John Smith, *Synonyms Discriminated*. (London, 1901), p. 429.

5. The Chinese correlated the organs and meridians with certain emotions. This is a comprehensive and verifiable approach. See Dr. Felix Mann, *Acupuncture: Cure of Many Diseases*. (London: Heinemann, 1971), p. 51.

THE GOAL

1. It is not without significance that the ancient Chinese believed that the Chi first entered the lung meridian and from there travelled through the body to the various other meridians and channels of energy.

2. For more on the concept of breath and spirit, see Ron DelBene, The *Breath of Life: A Simple Way to Pray*. (Minneapolis: Winston Press, 1981).

3. James Hastings, ed. *Encyclopedia of Religion and Ethics*. (New York: Scribners, 1920), Vol. XI, p. 784.

4. John Diamond, *The Collected Papers of John Diamond*, M.D. (Valley Cottage: Archaeus Press, 1977), Vol. I, pp. 34-49.

5. Xanthippe was the wife of Socrates, "notorious...for the stories of her bad temper." This phrase was used by Franz Josef Haydn to describe his wife. Unlike my patient, Haydn fortunately had his music.

INTRODUCTION TO ACUPUNCTURE

1. See, for example, Mary Austin, Acupuncture Therapy, ASI Publishers, New York, 1972, and Felix Mann, The Meridians of Acupuncture, London, Wm. Heinemann Medical Books, 1971. These are called *meridian alarm points*.

2. Of course, if he says the positive affirmations for the thymus, then all meridian imbalances will automatically be corrected.

3. Temporarily relieved by the "cocktail hour"

4. It is not necessary in most cases to test both sides of bilateral points, although in some instances when you experience difficulty in arriving at a conclusion it is required. This is not a frequent occurrence.

THE MERIDIANS AND THEIR EMOTIONS

1. You may find as you begin to undertake some of the testing in this chapter that some subjects are strengthened by what appears to be an inappropriate affirmation. For example, when you should be strengthened by saying, "I am full of joy," you may be strengthened as well by saying, "I am happy." These responses are not common, but when they occur it is often because the subject's own understanding of the meaning of the word is very generalised and perhaps confused. Merely explain the specific definitions to the subject and retest. Considering how imprecise our language has become, it is surprising how rarely this situation occurs.

2. "An Introduction to Psycho-Etymology," *Collected Papers of John Diamond, M.D.*, Volume II, (Valley Cottage: Archaeus Press, 1980), pp. 139-157. For an example of the psychoanalytic approach to etymology, refer to Ernest Jones, *On the Nightmare* (London: Hogarth Press, 1949).

3. Owen Barfield, *Poetic Diction: A Study in Meaning* (New York: McGraw-Hill, 1964), pp. 63-64.

4. When testing these meridian types, you will find that most people will test strong in the clear and weak when they test-touch the point for the specific meridian involved. Some people who are more vulnerable to the particular stress being introduced may test weak in the clear. It will be found for those people that touching the test point at the same time, through some mechanism which is not well understood, will cause them to test strong. This indicates that the specific meridian is involved, but that the energy loss has been greater than usual.

5. For a comprehensive list of dictionaries consulted for definitions throughout this chapter, see Appendix I, p. 155.

6. Richard Crashaw, "The Hymn of St. Thomas in Adoration of the Blessed Sacrament."

7. Carl D. Buck, *A Dictionary of Selected Synonyms in the Principal Indo-European Languages* (Chicago: University of Chicago Press, 1965).

8. Vol. V, 15th edition, 1978, p. 179.

9. Aeschylus, *The Agamemnon,* tr. Gilbert Murray (London: Allen &

Unwin, 1961), p. xiv.

10. in Melanie Klein *Envy and Gratitude & Other Works* 1946-1963 (New York: Delta, 1975), p. 280.

11. E. R. Dodds, *The Greeks and the Irrational* (Berkeley: University of California Press, 1951), p. 31.

12. Adrian Stokes, *Greek Culture and the Ego* (London: Tavistock, 1958), p. 22.

13. William Whateley, *Prototypes or the primarie precedent* (1639).

14. *The Philosophy of Spinoza* (New York: Modern Library, 1927), p. xviii.

15. You may recall in this context the frequency with which alcoholics develop liver disease. We now see how we must deal with their emotional factors in addition to their nutritional deficiencies.

16. The word *splenetic* has no relationship to the emotional states that accompany the spleen meridian. Its first usage was to do with depression, and then later it evolved to its present usage—to have "an irritable or morose or peevish disposition or temperament; given or liable to fits of angry impatience or irritability; ill-humoured, testy, irascible," related to the heart meridian emotions. (see p. 71).

17. John Diamond, M.D., *The Re-Mothering Experience* (Valley Cottage: Archaeus Press, 1981), pp. 63-68.

18. John Diamond, M.D., *The Life Energy in Music* (Valley Cottage: Archaeus Press, 1981), Vol. I, pp. 124 - 131.

19. Hanna Segal, *Introduction to the Work of Melanie Klein* (London: Hogarth Press, 1973), p. ix.

20. Acts 18:6 "I am clean." Joshua 2:19 "We will be guiltless." Luke 11:41 "And, behold, all things are clean unto you."

21. But, as we now know, sorrow and disappointment are not functions of the circulation-sex meridian at all, but they are related to the small intestine and stomach meridians respectively.

22. William Cowper, *The Task.*

23. Percy Bysshe Shelley, *Queen Mab, a philosophical poem* (1813)

1. Robert Burton, *The Anatomy of Melancholy* (1621).

25. Owen Meridith, *Lucile* (1860).

26. See also "A Psychological Notation on the Root Gn, Kn, Cn," by Henry A. Bunker and Bertram D. Lewin, in *Psychoanalysis and Culture*, eds. G. B. Wilbur and Warner Muensterberger (New York: International Universities Press, 1951), pp. 363 - 367.

27. The *Oxford English Dictionary* defines resentment as "a strong feeling of ill will or anger against the author or authors of a wrong or affront."

28. Charles Darwin, *Expression of the Emotions in Man and Animals* (New York: Philosophical Library, 1955).

29. People who are bitter themselves often suffer from "sour stomach."

30. Segal, op. cit., p. 40.

31. Theodore Reik, *The Haunting Melody* (New York: Grove Press, 1953).

32. John Bowlby, *Maternal Care and Mental Health*, Monograph Series, no. 2, World Health Organization, Geneva, 1951.

33. Morris B. Parloff, "The Me Degeneration", *Psychology Today* (December 1979), p. 92.

34. Simultaneous contradictory messages. see pp. 214-217.

35. In the Editor's Note to the introduction of Freud's "Mourning and Melancholia" (Vol. XIV of the Standard Edition of the *Complete Psychological Works),* we read that Freud included under the term melancholia "what are now usually described as states of depression."

36. Eric Partridge, *Origins—Short Etymological Dictionary of Modern English* (London: Routledge and Kegan Paul, 1966).

37. Lady M. W. Montagu, *Letter to Miss A. Wortley* (1709).

38. The interested reader is referred to C. S. Lewis, Studies in Words (Cambridge: Cambridge University Press, 1960, 1967), chapter 3.

39. Of course, one can also have tears of anger (heart meridian).

40. Excerpt from *Diamond Report* No. 66, August 1982.

41. From *Diamond Report* No. 56, October 1981.

42. H. Bailey and M. Love, *A Short Practice of Surgery* (London: H. K. Lewis & Co. Ltd., 1971, fifteenth edition), p. 848.

DEEPER LAYERS

1. We must remember that frequently, for proper deep testing, we go through many levels to reveal what is beneath each layer. Here we are concentrating upon revealing successively deeper layers, not levels, of the individual.

THE DOUBLE-BIND

1. Gregory Bateson, et al, "Toward a Theory of Schizophrenia," *Behavioral Science*, 1:251, 1956.

DAILY PROGRAM

1. See Diamond, *Your Body Doesn't Lie.*

2. Put your tongue against the roof of your mouth, with the tip about a quarter of an inch behind the upper front teeth. This is a strengthening position. (See Diamond, *Your Body Doesn't Lie*).

3. It is preferable that you say the affirmations aloud. Your own voice will strengthen and reinforce the affirmations.

TRANSMUTATION

1. The New Columbia Encyclopedia (New York: Columbia University Press, 1975), p. 2236.

Appendix III

It has been found, primarily through the work of Dr. George Goodheart, the originator of applied kinesiology (from which the use of the muscle test discussed in this book is derived), that certain food supplements can be beneficial for specific meridian imbalances. If you find that one or two meridians are consistently testing weak over a period of time, then it may be advisable, with proper nutritional guidance, to help reactivate these meridians with appropriate support. Of course, these should always be tested individually to ensure their effectiveness in each specific case.

A number of vitamin companies now market concentrated extracts of whole glands in tablet form. These are quite distinct from hormone preparations, which may be derived from the glands.

Nutritional support can be very valuable, but it is just that—it is a support. I believe what is basically required is on the one hand working with the underlying psychological factors that produce the meridian weakness, and on the other, getting nutritional information and other guidance and therapy from the appropriate health professionals.

MERIDIAN	SOME BASIC SUPPLEMENTS
Thymus	Thymus concentrate.
Lung	Lung concentrate. Vitamin C.
Liver	Liver concentrate. Bile salts. Vitamins A, "F." *
Liver	Kali. Sulph.
Gall Bladder	Bile salts. Vitamin A.
Spleen.**	Vitamins C, "F." G.
	or Pancreatic concentrate. Betaine hydrochloride.
	Vitamins A, B_1

* Qualitatively derived unsaturated fatty acids (arachidonic, linoleic and linolenic), sometimes unofficially referred to as "vitamin F."
** Spleen meridian relates to both spleen and pancreas.

MERIDIAN	SOME BASIC SUPPLEMENTS
Kidney	Kidney concentrate. Chlorophyll. Vitamins A, B_1, B_2, C, E, "F."
Large Intestine	Lactobacillus acidophilus. Chlorophyll. Wheat Germ Oil. Vitamins A, B_1, C, D, E.
Circulation-Sex*	Adrenal concentrate. Vitamin C. or (male) Prostate and testicular concentrates. Vitamin E. or (female) Ovarian and uterine concentrates. Vitamin E.
Heart	Heart concentrate. Vitamins B. and/or B_2,** E.
Stomach	Stomach concentrate. Betaine hydrochloride. Vitamins B_1, B_2, B_3, B_6.
Thyroid	Thyroid concentrate. Sea vegetables. Iodine. Vitamin C.
Small Intestine	Duodenal concentrate. Vitamins B_1, D, E.
Bladder	Wheat germ oil. Vitamins A, B_1, C, E.

TISSUE SALTS

The twelve tissue salts are low-potency homoeopathic remedies. Dr. Schuessler suggested over a hundred years ago that these twelve salts were essential to the life of a cell.*** His theory was that when the salts in the cells were balanced, then health would be facilitated. While medical science may not approve of his biochemical principles, nonetheless, each activates a specific meridian. Thus, life energy may be enhanced through the rebalancing of the acupuncture system of the body, which these tissue salts can help achieve. Again, as with the food supplements, it is not recommended that they be used for transitory imbalances, but rather when a consistent pattern emerges, such as persistent underactivity of a meridian over a period of time.

While these tissue salts are available in health food stores, it is of course always best that they be used with the guidance of a qualified health practitioner. I usually recommend that tissue salts be taken for not more than a few weeks.

* Circulation-sex meridian relates to both adrenal glands and reproductive glands.
** Should be tested individually.
*** J. B. Chapman, *Dr. Schuessler's Biochemistry* (London New Era, 1961).

MERIDIAN	TISSUE SALT
Lung	Silica
Liver	Kali. Sulph.
Gall Bladder	Calc. Phos.
Spleen	Kali. Mur.
Kidney	Ferr. Phos.
Large Intestine	Nat. Mur.
Circulation-Sex	Nat. Phos.
Heart	Nat. Sulph.
Stomach	Calc. Sulph.
Thyroid	Calc. Fluor.
Small Intestine	Kali. Phos.
Bladder	Mag. Phos.

Index

About the Author

DR. JOHN DIAMOND graduated cum laude from Sydney University Medical School in 1957, and was awarded the Naughton-Manning Prize for Psychiatry. In Australia, he held many senior clinical and university teaching appointments in clinical psychiatry. After going to the United States, Dr. Diamond served as an attending psychiatrist at New York's Beth Israel Medical Centre and held a professorship of psychiatry at Mount Sinai Medical School, also in New York City. Board certified in psychiatry in both Great Britain and Australia, Dr. Diamond is a member of the Royal Australian and New Zealand College of Psychiatrists and of the Royal College of Psychiatry of Great Britain.

From the seventies, Dr. Diamond expanded his practice to include preventive medicine and held many positions in that field. He is a fellow and was past president of the International Academy of Preventive Medicine.

During his forty years in medicine, Dr. Diamond has lectured to many professional organisations, both nationally and internationally. Through the Institute of Behavioural Kinesiology, an organisation now based in South Salem, New York, Dr. Diamond currently conducts research and teaches the theories and practical applications of Behavioural Kinesiology.